PRENTICE HALL
LITERATURE

PENGUIN EDITION

Teaching Resources

Unit 5
Drama

D1451598

Grade Seven

PEARSON

Prentice
Hall

Upper Saddle River, New Jersey
Boston, Massachusetts

ISBN 0-13-165195-1

1 2 3 4 5 6 7 8 9 10   09 08 07 06 05

BD

Contents

Part 1 Purpose for Reading

from **Dragonwings** by Laurence Yep
Vocabulary Warm-up Word Lists

Study these words from Dragonwings. *Then, apply your knowledge to the activities that follow.*

Word List A

audience [AW dee uhns] *n.* group of watchers or listeners
   The <u>audience</u> applauded wildly after the exciting performance.

contraption [kuhn TRAP shuhn] *n.* odd device or gadget
   The strange <u>contraption</u> had weird levers and buttons, so we didn't know how to start it.

demonstration [dem uhn STRAY shuhn] *n.* outward showing
   In <u>demonstration</u> of her anger, Cassie stamped her foot.

flight [FLYT] *adj.* relating to the act or manner of flying
   Hector wanted to be a pilot, so he enrolled in <u>flight</u> school.

haul [HAWL] *v.* pull with force; drag
   Bruce and Cara <u>haul</u> their equipment from the car to the campsite.

repeat [ree PEET] *v.* to do over again
   Samantha will <u>repeat</u> her talent-show performance on Friday.

serious [SEER ee uhs] *adj.* giving cause for concern; dangerous
   After a <u>serious</u> car accident, Bryan was taken to the hospital.

steep [STEEP] *adj.* having a sharp slope or incline
   The mountain we climbed is very <u>steep</u> and high.

Word List B

expected [ek SPEKT ed] *v.* looked for as likely to happen
   Casey <u>expected</u> a raise in her allowance when she turned twelve.

immigration [im i GRAY shun] *adj.* coming into a foreign country to live there
   Mr. Moreno checked Lupe's <u>immigration</u> status before hiring her.

laundry [LAWN dree] *n.* commercial establishment for washing and ironing clothing
   The <u>laundry</u> is a profitable family business for the Johnsons.

machines [muh SHEENZ] *n.* mechanical devices or equipment
   Sixteen sewing <u>machines</u> were set up in four rows in the factory.

merchants [MER chuhnts] *n.* persons who buy and sell things for profit; storekeepers
   Stu and Don had been <u>merchants</u> at the same location for ten years.

probably [PRAHB uh blee] *adv.* likely; presumably
   The weather is good, so the plane will <u>probably</u> land on time.

recover [ree KUHV uhr] *v.* to get well
   It took Steven ten days to <u>recover</u> from the flu.

separated [SEP uh rayt ed] *v.* came apart
   The glue was weak, so the decorations <u>separated</u> from the frame.

from *Dragonwings* by Laurence Yep
Vocabulary Warm-up Exercises

Exercise A *Fill in each blank in the paragraph below with an appropriate word from Word List A. Use each word only once.*

Nobody could figure out how to use the strange [1] _____, so they had to ask Jack, the inventor, for a [2] _____. A group of assistants helped Jack [3] _____ the machine to the stage. The [4] _____ watched as Jack pressed a red button. Suddenly the propeller began turning. Jack, standing too close, got hit by the twisting blades. His assistants thought he was hurt, but it was not [5] _____. "Let me [6] _____ what I said earlier," said Jack. "This machine can push heavy loads up [7] _____ inclines. For example, a [8] _____ attendant could easily push a serving cart to the front of the plane, even if the plane were still ascending!"

Exercise B *Answer the questions with complete sentences or explanations.*

1. Why might egg yolks and egg whites be <u>separated</u>?

   _____

2. If you <u>expected</u> to win a special award, what preparations might you make?

   _____

3. Name two <u>machines</u> you might use at home.

   _____

4. What does an <u>immigration</u> officer do?

   _____

5. If you dropped your clothes off at a <u>laundry</u>, what would you want done with them?

   _____

6. What do <u>merchants</u> do to earn money?

   _____

7. If Alex says he will <u>probably</u> go to a party, will he be there for sure?

   _____

8. How long did it take you to <u>recover</u> the last time you got sick?

   _____

from **Dragonwings** by Laurence Yep
Reading Warm-up A

Read the following passage. Pay special attention to the underlined words. Then, read it again, and complete the activities. Use a separate sheet of paper for your written answers.

Imagine for a moment that you are with the Wright brothers near Kitty Hawk, North Carolina. The year is 1903. It is eight days before Christmas. You are excited to be among the small underline(audience) waiting to see if they will actually fly this time. Besides you and the Wrights, four men and a boy are there to witness this demonstration.

Yesterday, Wilbur had made an attempt, but the contraption they called an "aeroplane" had barely made it off the ground. Would today be any different? Yesterday, they had tried to fly from the top of a steep hill. Today, they would try to take off from flat ground instead. By aiming the plane into the wind, they figured they had a better chance to get aloft.

The men had helped the Wrights haul the plane to the sand bar at Kitty Hawk. It weighs about 600 pounds, and its two pairs of wings are about 40 feet across, so it had been quite a job to get it in place. Now, you watch as Orville climbs out on the lower wing. He stretches out face down. His legs hang out beyond the wing. Wilbur ties a strap around his brother's hips so he won't fall off. Wilbur starts the engine as Orville grips the controls. The plane moves forward, rising ten feet in the air. The boy who's watching this with you starts shouting. "He's flying! He's flying!" One of the men takes a photograph. The flight time is 12 seconds, as Orville flies 120 feet. The brothers take turns flying a few more times that day. The longest flight is done by Wilbur, who flies 852 feet in 59 seconds.

A strong wind finally tips the plane over. The damage is serious, and the plane needs major repairs. Soon, though, the Wrights plan to repeat the experiment, and you hope they'll invite you again.

1. Underline the sentence that tells how many people are in the small audience. What did you see the last time you were part of an *audience*?

2. Underline the words that tell what the audience will do at the demonstration. Use *demonstration* in a sentence.

3. Circle the word that tells what the Wrights called their contraption. Use *contraption* in a sentence.

4. Underline the word that means the opposite of steep. Would you rather climb a *steep* hill or walk on a flat beach? Explain.

5. Circle the words that tell where the men had to haul the plane. Describe the last time you had to *haul* something heavy from one place to another.

6. Underline the phrases that give information about the flight time, or how far they went and how fast. What does *flight* mean?

7. Circle the words that explain why the damage is considered serious. Write a sentence using the word *serious*.

8. Underline the words that tell what the Wrights plan to repeat. What does *repeat* mean?

Name _____ Date _____

from **Dragonwings** by Laurence Yep
Reading Warm-up B

Read the following passage. Pay special attention to the underlined words. Then, read it again, and complete the activities. Use a separate sheet of paper for your written answers.

After the Civil War, people from other countries began moving to the United States in great numbers. In part, this was due to the abolition of slavery. In need of a cheap labor pool to <u>recover</u> from the war, America welcomed the poor, who <u>expected</u> to work for very little pay. Most of these immigrants came from Germany, Ireland, and England. A smaller percentage of the immigrants came from China.

The Chinese had first been drawn to this country by the California gold rush that began in 1849. As they came through the <u>immigration</u> station in San Francisco, they were welcomed at first. This is <u>probably</u> because they worked hard and kept to themselves. They were also willing to accept low pay. Most of these immigrants were young male peasants. They had left their rural villages to labor in the American West. <u>Separated</u> from their families, they worked on the railroads. They also mined for gold and other minerals.

As these economic opportunities declined, the Chinese looked elsewhere for work. Some opened businesses that did <u>laundry</u> for people who didn't want to wash and iron their own clothes. Others took low-paying factory jobs, working at various <u>machines</u> to produce manufactured goods.

By the 1870s, hard times forced other groups to compete with the Chinese for humble jobs. Hostility toward the Chinese soon developed. In 1882, Congress passed the Chinese Exclusion Act; between 1882 and 1965, only <u>merchants</u> (such as shopkeepers and traders), diplomats, and students and their dependents were allowed to travel to the United States.

Laws passed in the 1960s restored many basic rights to Chinese Americans. Since the 1970s, two types of Chinese immigrants have been coming to the United States. The first group is wealthy and well-educated. The second group includes those who are fleeing poverty and other hardships.

1. Underline the words that tell from what America needed to <u>recover</u>. What might you do to try to *recover* from a disappointment?

2. Circle the words that tell what the poor immigrants <u>expected</u>. Write a sentence using the word *expected*.

3. Underline the words that tell what happened when the Chinese arrived at the <u>immigration</u> station. What does *immigration* mean?

4. Circle the words that explain why these immigrants were <u>probably</u> welcomed at first. Then, rewrite the sentence, replacing *probably* with words that have a similar meaning.

5. Underline the words that tell from whom the immigrants were <u>separated</u>. Use *separated* in a sentence.

6. Circle the words that describe customers for the <u>laundry</u>. What items might you find at a *laundry*?

7. Underline the words that tell what the <u>machines</u> did. What are *machines*?

8. Circle the words that further explain what <u>merchants</u> are. Use *merchants* in a sentence.

Name _____ Date _____

Laurence Yep
Listening and Viewing

Segment 1: Meet Laurence Yep
- Why did Laurence Yep identify with the themes he encountered in science fiction?
- Does it surprise you that he chose to write science fiction? Why or why not?

_____

_____

_____

Segment 2: Drama
- According to Yep, what are the differences between a drama and a novel?
- Which form, the drama or the novel, might be more difficult to write? Why?

_____

_____

_____

Segment 3: The Writing Process
- Why does Yep adjust his drafts as he writes?
- What method of Yep's would you be most inclined to try in your own writing? Why?

_____

_____

_____

Segment 4: The Rewards of Writing
- What does Yep think literature can do for young readers?

_____

_____

_____

_____

Learning About Drama

Drama is a story told in dialogue by performers in front of an audience. The **playwright** is the author of a drama, which may also be called a *play.* The play itself is written in segments, called **acts.** Acts are often divided into **scenes.**

A playwright uses **characterization** to create believable characters. To advance the action, the playwright creates **dramatic speech.** Two types of dramatic speech are **dialogue,** conversation between two or more characters, and **monologue,** a long speech by a single character. A monologue often reveals a character's thoughts and feelings.

Stage directions describe the scenery and tell how the characters move and speak. The **set** is the construction onstage that suggests the time and place of the action (the setting). **Props** are small movable items that make the set look realistic.

Two types of drama are comedy and tragedy. A **comedy** has a happy ending. It often features ordinary characters in funny situations. In a **tragedy,** the events lead to the downfall of the main character. The main character may be an ordinary person, but the traditional tragic hero is a man of great significance, such as a king.

A. DIRECTIONS: *Read the following excerpt from a drama. Then, answer the questions.*

[*The FISCHERS' kitchen, 7 A.M. MRS. FISCHER sits at kitchen table, reading a newspaper. The door opens. BECKY rushes in. She wears school clothes and carries a book bag.*]

BECKY. Mom! I overslept! I'll miss the tryouts for the play. Why didn't you wake me?

MRS. FISCHER [*getting up from the table*]. Calm down. Let me make you some breakfast.

BECKY [*almost shouting*]. Breakfast? I'm already late!

MRS. FISCHER [*patiently*]. No, dear, you're early. It's Saturday. Tryouts aren't until Monday.

1. Describe the set. _____

2. What props are used? _____

3. Quote a stage direction that tells how a character speaks.

   _____

4. Quote a stage direction that tells how a character moves.

   _____

5. Is the passage a dialogue or a monologue? Explain.

   _____

6. Is this scene more likely from a comedy or a tragedy? Explain. _____

   _____

from **Dragonwings** by Laurence Yep
Model Selection: Drama

Dragonwings is a **drama,** or *play,* a story told in dialogue and meant to be performed by actors before an audience. Laurence Yep is the **playwright,** the author of the play. A play is written in segments. You have read just one segment, a **scene.** In a full-length work, several scenes usually make up an **act,** and several acts make up the play.

To advance the action, Yep wrote **dramatic speech.** Most of the excerpt from *Dragonwings* contains **dialogue,** conversation between several characters. One section might be considered a **monologue,** a long speech by a single character. A monologue often reveals a character's thoughts and feelings.

Stage directions describe the scenery and sound effects and tell how the characters move and speak. The **set** is the construction onstage that suggests the time and place of the action (the setting). **Props** are small movable items that make the set look realistic.

In a drama, as the **main character** develops, the audience should identify with his or her emotions. The **climax** of a drama, the moment of greatest tension, concerns the main character in some way. With the climax comes some insight or revelation.

A. DIRECTIONS: *Answer these questions about Scene 9 of* Dragonwings.

1. What is the setting? _____

2. What props is Moon Shadow most likely using during his opening speech?

   _____

3. Describe one sound effect that is used. _____

4. After Windrider takes off in the airplane, Moon Shadow speaks these lines:

   I thought he'd fly forever and ever. Up, up to heaven and never come down. But then . . .
   Dragonwings came crashing to earth. Father had a few broken bones, but it was nothing
   serious. Only the aeroplane was wrecked. . . . Father didn't say much, just thought a lot I
   figured he was busy designing the next aeroplane. . . .

   What type of dramatic speech would you call this passage? Explain your answer.

   _____

5. Who is the main character? How can you tell?

   _____

B. DIRECTIONS: *What is the climax of events in Scene 9 of* Dragonwings? *What insight does Windrider gain in response to the climax? What insight does Moon Shadow gain?*

_____

_____

_____

Name _____   Date _____

from **Dragonwings** by Laurence Yep
Selection Test A

Learning About Drama *Identify the letter of the choice that best answers the question.*

____ 1. Which of the following is the best definition of drama?
   A. a story with props
   B. a story with a happy ending
   C. a story told in dialogue by performers
   D. a story in which the main character eventually fails

____ 2. Which statement correctly describes a monologue?
   A. A monologue is a serious speech spoken only in a tragedy.
   B. A monologue is a short speech spoken by one character.
   C. A monologue is a long speech spoken by one character.
   D. A monologue is a conversation between several characters.

____ 3. Which term describes the constructions that suggest the time and place of the action of a play?
   A. stage
   B. set
   C. act
   D. scene

____ 4. Which of the following is an example of a prop?
   A. a door at the back of the stage
   B. a pair of crutches that a character uses
   C. a direction telling how a character moves
   D. a long speech in the opening scene

____ 5. Which line contains a stage direction that tells how the actor playing John should speak?
   A. JOHN [*throwing his book*]. I don't understand the problem.
   B. JOHN. What time does the physics test begin?
   C. JOHN [*shaking his head*]. I'll never be a rocket scientist.
   D. JOHN [*pleading*]. You've got to help me.

____ 6. Which statement is true of every comedy?
   A. It has a happy ending.
   B. It contains sound effects.
   C. It contains unusal animals.
   D. It features at least one clown.

Name _____ Date _____

Critical Reading

_____ 7. The first line of Scene 9 of *Dragonwings* is:

    Piedmont, later that day, outside the stable.

What does this line tell the reader?

A. which characters are onstage

B. where and when the scene takes place

C. how the characters are to act

D. whether this is a comedy or a tragedy

_____ 8. At the beginning of Scene 9 of *Dragonwings*, Moon Shadow is writing a letter. To whom is he writing?

A. Miss Whitlaw

B. Black Dog

C. his uncle

D. his mother

_____ 9. What is the relationship between Moon Shadow and Windrider in *Dragonwings*?

A. Windrider is Moon Shadow's brother.

B. Windrider is Moon Shadow's uncle.

C. Windrider is Moon Shadow's father.

D. Windrider is Moon Shadow's teacher.

_____ 10. Which statement is true about Uncle Bright Star in *Dragonwings*?

A. He has come to help although he does not think the plane will fly.

B. He refuses to help because he thinks planes are unreliable.

C. He is worried that Moon Shadow will not speak to him again.

D. He is angry because Windrider has refused to return to China.

_____ 11. In Scene 9 of *Dragonwings*, what action do the characters perform without props, in a pantomime?

A. taking the harness off Uncle's horse

B. dragging the plane to the top of the hill

C. pulling down on the propellers of the plane

D. reading a newspaper article about the flight

_____ 12. What does Uncle Bright Star do in Scene 9 of *Dragonwings* to help the characters work together?

A. He turns the propeller.

B. He drives the wagon.

C. He dances a ballet.

D. He leads a chant.

____ 13. What is the purpose of Windrider's ballet in Scene 9 of *Dragonwings*?
    A. to show how creative he is
    B. to emphasize his love for Moon Shadow
    C. to express his hopes for the future
    D. to represent the flight of the airplane

____ 14. What do the sound effects in Scene 9 of *Dragonwings* allow the audience to hear?
    A. the movement of the horse
    B. the cheering of the crowds
    C. the flight of the plane
    D. the crash of the plane

____ 15. After the plane takes off in Scene 9 of *Dragonwings*, what happens to it?
    A. It grows smaller and then disappears.
    B. Windrider sells it to start a laundry.
    C. It crashes to the ground and breaks apart.
    D. It glides to the ground but is not damaged.

Essay

16. Toward the end of Scene 9 of *Dragonwings*, Windrider tells Moon Shadow that he has decided to give up flying to go to work in a laundry and bring his wife from China. In an essay, tell what those decisions say about Windrider. What kind of man is he? How has he changed? Mention two details from the scene to support your ideas.

17. At the end of Scene 9 of *Dragonwings*, Moon Shadow says that he and his father talked about flying but they never actually flew again. Moon Shadow says,

    But dreams stay with you, and we never forgot.

In an essay, tell what you think Moon Shadow means by these lines.

from **Dragonwings** by Laurence Yep
Selection Test B

Learning About Drama *Identify the letter of the choice that best completes the statement or answers the question.*

____ 1. A book that a character reads in a scene from a play is an example of
    A. a stage direction.   C. a prop.
    B. a set.   D. a monologue.

____ 2. Which of the following is the best definition of dialogue?
    A. a conversation between characters in a play
    B. the conflict that the characters in a play face
    C. the downfall of the main character in a play
    D. a long speech by a character in a play

____ 3. Stage directions may indicate
    I. the tone of voice an actor should use
    II. an action an actor should take
    III. the scenery
    IV. sound effects
    A. I and II
    B. I, II, and IV
    C. III and IV
    D. I, II, III, and IV

____ 4. Which statement is true of every tragedy?
    A. The events lead to a happy ending.
    B. The main character is someone of significance.
    C. The events lead to the downfall of the main character.
    D. The main character reveals his or her inner thoughts at the climax.

____ 5. Which statement is true of a screenplay?
    A. It is better suited to comedy than to tragedy.
    B. It contains dialogue but never includes a monologue.
    C. The stage directions do not refer to the setting.
    D. The stage directions may refer to camera angles.

____ 6. Which statement is true of every comedy?
    A. The main character is very funny.
    B. Clowns appear in one or more scenes.
    C. The ending is a happy one.
    D. The characters are unrealistic.

Critical Reading

____ 7. Scene 9 of *Dragonwings* is set
    A. outside a stable.
    B. in a stable.
    C. in a laundry near San Francisco.
    D. at Uncle Bright Star's home in Piedmont.

____ 8. What event takes place as Scene 9 of *Dragonwings* opens?
   A. Uncle Bright Star stamps his feet to get everyone moving.
   B. Miss Whitlaw knocks on the door of the stable.
   C. Moon Shadow writes a letter to his mother.
   D. Windrider climbs into his airplane.

____ 9. At the beginning of Scene 9 of *Dragonwings*, the audience learns that Moon Shadow
   A. owes Miss Whitlaw a lot of money.
   B. has lost everything to Black Dog.
   C. is about to move back to China.
   D. does not believe airplanes can fly.

____ 10. In Scene 9 of *Dragonwings*, why is Moon Shadow surprised that Uncle Bright Star has come to help?
   A. Uncle Bright Star is old and in poor health.
   B. Uncle Bright Star has stolen from Windrider.
   C. Uncle Bright Star has traveled a great distance.
   D. Uncle Bright Star does not believe the plane will fly.

____ 11. In Scene 9 of *Dragonwings*, Windrider and the others go through the motions of pulling on ropes without actually using ropes. In doing so, they are
   A. using sound effects.
   B. using props.
   C. pantomiming.
   D. dancing.

____ 12. In Scene 9 of *Dragonwings*, the characters must drag the plane to the top of the hill because
   A. the wheels on the plane have gotten hopelessly stuck in the mud.
   B. the winds at the top of the hill are blowing in the right direction.
   C. Red Rabbit is too tired to pull everyone up the hill in the wagon.
   D. Miss Whitlaw has asked them to take the plane off her property.

____ 13. Uncle Bright Star starts a chant in Scene 9 of *Dragonwings* because
   A. he believes that if he prays, the plane will fly.
   B. he wants to impress Miss Whitlaw with his knowledge.
   C. he believes a chant will give Windrider confidence.
   D. he wants everyone to work at the same pace.

____ 14. In Scene 9 of *Dragonwings*, Windrider does a ballet in order to
   A. represent the act of flying a plane.
   B. thank Uncle Bright Star for helping.
   C. provide Miss Whitlaw with entertainment.
   D. demonstrate an aspect of his culture.

____ 15. What event occurs at the climax of Scene 9 of *Dragonwings*?
   A. Uncle Bright Star joins Windrider in the airplane.
   B. Dragonwings starts to fall but then levels off.
   C. Windrider succeeds in making the plane fly.
   D. Moon Shadow's mother reveals her secret.

____ 16. At the end of Scene 9 of *Dragonwings*, Moon Shadow
   A. gives his cap to his father.
   B. appears onstage as an adult.
   C. decides that he will someday fly a plane.
   D. decides to return to China to visit his mother.

____ 17. According to Scene 9 of *Dragonwings*, the flight of Dragonwings is not a complete success because
   A. the plane crashes and breaks apart.
   B. Windrider flies off and never returns.
   C. Windrider vows never to fly again.
   D. Miss Whitlaw is disappointed.

____ 18. At the end of Scene 9 of *Dragonwings*, Uncle Bright Star offers
   A. to bring Windrider's wife from China.
   B. to help Windrider build a new airplane.
   C. Windrider the money to return to China.
   D. Windrider a partnership in his laundry.

____ 19. At the end of Scene 9 of *Dragonwings*, what is suggested will likely happen?
   A. Uncle Bright Star will make a lot of money.
   B. Windrider will become a commercial pilot.
   C. Miss Whitlaw will have the airplane repaired.
   D. Moon Shadow's mother will come from China.

____ 20. Who is the main character of *Dragonwings*?
   A. Windrider
   B. Uncle Bright Star
   C. Miss Whitlaw
   D. Moon Shadow

Essay

21. At the end of Scene 9 of *Dragonwings*, Windrider hands his cap to Moon Shadow. In an essay, explain what this action might symbolize. Why does Moon Shadow wear the cap at the end of the scene, when he appears as an adult?

22. At the end of Scene 9 of *Dragonwings*, Moon Shadow appears as an adult and puts on Windrider's cap. He says,

   We always talked about flying again. Only we never did. . . . But dreams stay with you, and we never forgot.

In an essay, explain what these last lines tell you. How would the scene have been different if it had ended just before, with Windrider speaking the final lines?

Name _____   Starting Date _____   Ending Date _____

Unit 5: Drama
Part 1 Concept Map

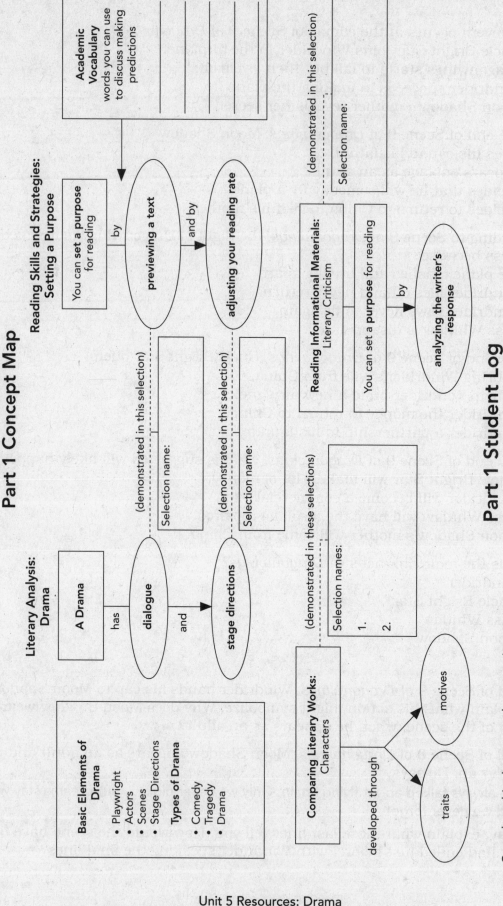

Academic Vocabulary words you can use to discuss making predictions

_____
_____
_____

Reading Skills and Strategies:
Setting a Purpose

You can set a purpose for reading

by → previewing a text

and by → adjusting your reading rate

(demonstrated in this selection)
Selection name:

(demonstrated in this selection)
Selection name:

Literary Analysis:
Drama

A Drama

has → dialogue

and → stage directions

Basic Elements of Drama
- Playwright
- Actors
- Scenes
- Stage Directions

Types of Drama
- Comedy
- Tragedy
- Drama

Comparing Literary Works:
Characters

developed through → motives

traits

(demonstrated in these selections)
Selection names:
1.
2.

Reading Informational Materials:
Literary Criticism

You can set a **purpose** for reading

by → analyzing the writer's response

(demonstrated in this selection)
Selection name:

Part 1 Student Log

Complete this chart to track your assignments.

Writing	Extend Your Learning	Writing Workshop	Other Assignments

14

Unit 5: Drama
Part 1 Diagnostic Test 9

MULTIPLE CHOICE

Read the selection. Then, answer the questions that follow.

Mangrove trees grow along tropical shores, including the southern Gulf Coast of Florida. They can live in the muck and shallow water along the coast because, unlike most other trees, they can survive in salty water. Their roots form a thick latticework that looks like twisted stilts. Some of these roots take in air so that the tree can "breathe" in the mud. These amazing trees grow in mangrove keys, or low-lying islands, and play an important role in the ecosystem of the Gulf Coast.

In mangrove keys, tiny marine creatures hatch and feed among the mangrove roots. These creatures become food for shrimp, other shellfish, and fish. Those, in turn, become food for birds and turtles. All of these creatures may wind up as food for crocodiles.

During a storm, the Gulf may flood a key. Then, in the area between thick growths of trees, wading birds forage for food. An egret stirs up mangrove roots to find a fish, a frog, or insects. A heron dips its long beak into the water and comes up with dinner.

These mangrove keys are important to many creatures. In recent years, people have realized that they must help protect the balance of life there.

1. What is one way mangrove trees are different from other trees?
   A. They grow near the water.   C. They take in air.
   B. They grow very tall.   D. They can live in salt water.

2. Where do mangrove trees grow?
   A. on beaches   C. in central Florida
   B. along the shore in tropical regions D. along riverbanks

3. What are mangrove keys?
   A. areas near the shore that are key   C. low-lying islands on which mangroves
       points in the ecosystem   grow
   B. key-shaped structures made of the   D. areas of mangrove growth that open
       wood of the mangrove   out onto the ocean

4. Which of the following is true of mangrove trees?
   A. They grow in thick, rich soil.   C. They have thick, twisted, stilt-like roots.
   B. Their wood is of the highest quality. D. They have long, vine-like leaves.

5. Why are mangrove keys important to fish and shellfish?
   A. Mangrove keys have the pure water   C. Fish and shellfish are safe from preda-
       needed by fish and shellfish to   tors in mangrove keys.
       survive.   D. Mangrove keys are safe places from the
   B. They are rich feeding grounds for fish   many storms in the Gulf.
       and shellfish.

6. Which types of creatures are you likely to find in mangrove keys?
   A. whales and turtles
   B. frogs and swordfish
   C. deer and dolphins
   D. shrimp and crocodiles

7. What happens when a storm floods a mangrove key?
   A. Wading birds come to look for food.
   B. The mangrove key is destroyed.
   C. Most of the marine life is destroyed.
   D. Many of the trees collapse.

8. Why is it important to protect the mangrove keys?
   A. They are a rich ecosystem on which many creatures depend.
   B. They are part of the beautiful scenery of the Gulf.
   C. They are important areas for hunting and fishing.
   D. Many people depend on mangrove keys for their livelihood.

Read the selection. Then, answer the questions that follow.

Every fall, more than ten thousand people come from all around the world to a tiny town in Tennessee. They come to the National Storytelling Convention. Here, they listen to masters of the oral tradition tell their tales.

In 1973, Jimmy Neil Smith, mayor of Jonesborough, Tennessee, began the National Storytelling Convention. After hearing an extraordinarily well-told tale on the radio, he decided to start a storytelling festival. Then, people visiting from all parts of the world could hear the great stories and help keep them alive.

Today, the International Storytelling Center in Jonesborough helps spread appreciation for the power and importance of stories. The center reminds us that having a central place for people to meet was a part of all early societies. At this place, usually a fire pit, people made and ate food. They also celebrated and told stories there.

The center also feels that people might have more satisfactory relationships with one another as a result of sharing stories. So, it encourages us all to pass on our own stories. As we listen to one another and understand our stories, perhaps "we can transform our lives—and the world."

9. Where is the National Storytelling Convention held?
   A. around a great firepit
   B. in Jonesborough, Tennessee
   C. at the home of Jimmy Neil Smith
   D. in towns and cities around the country

10. How did Jimmy Neil Smith get the idea for a National Storytelling Convention?
    A. after watching a storyteller in action
    B. after hearing about other storytelling conventions
    C. after listening to a story on the radio
    D. after attending a storytelling convention in another town

11. What was Smith's purpose in starting a storytelling festival?
    A. to attract tourists to his town
    B. to help him win reelection as mayor
    C. to participate in storytelling activities
    D. to help keep great stories alive

12. Where did early societies meet to tell stories?
    A. around a fire pit
    B. at a storytelling center
    C. in caves during the winter
    D. at a meal

13. In early societies, what other things happened along with storytelling?

A. People formed hunting parties.

B. People established war councils.

C. People elected tribal leaders.

D. People feasted and celebrated.

14. Why was having a central place to meet and tell stories important to early societies?

A. Without a method of communication, people needed a meeting place.

B. People could get to know one another, share ideas, and celebrate together.

C. People needed to settle their differences without warfare.

D. People needed to make plans for improving their society.

15. How might sharing our own stories benefit us and others?

A. We might become accomplished storytellers.

B. We might be invited to the National Storytelling Convention.

C. We might get a better understanding of others.

D. People from other nations may be inspired to start storytelling festivals.

Vocabulary Warm-up Word Lists

Study these words from A Christmas Carol: Scrooge and Marley, *Act I. Then, complete the activities that follow.*

Word List A

gold [GOHLD] *n.* yellowish precious metal
    The <u>gold</u> used to make the necklace was of high quality.

lustrous [LUHS truhs] *adj.* shining or bright
    In the sunlight, Donna's hair looked shiny and <u>lustrous</u>.

miser [MY zuhr] *n.* stingy person who hoards his or her wealth
    Jay was a <u>miser</u> when it came to sharing his dessert with others.

penance [PEN uhns] *n.* voluntary act to show that one is sorry for a misdeed
    Ann decided that her <u>penance</u> for losing her temper with Molly was taking Molly to dinner.

perfection [puhr FEK shuhn] *n.* condition of being perfect or excellent
    The beautiful colors of the sunset were a vision of <u>perfection</u>.

replenish [ri PLEN ish] *v.* to make full or complete again by supplying a new stock
    Dot will <u>replenish</u> our supply of juice when she goes to the store.

resolute [REZ uh loot] *adj.* determined, unwavering
    With a <u>resolute</u> look, Alex set out to hike the entire length of the trail.

shrivels [SHRIV uhlz] *v.* wrinkles or becomes withered or shrunken
    The last rose of summer <u>shrivels</u> after it has bloomed.

Word List B

bleak [BLEEK] *adj.* cold, harsh, or dreary
    The constant rain gave us very damp, <u>bleak</u> weather.

dismal [DIZ muhl] *adj.* gloomy, miserable
    The <u>dismal</u> expression on Dave's face told us the race had not gone well.

establishments [i STAB lish muhntz] *n.* businesses; public or private structures
    The popular restaurant chain had many <u>establishments</u>.

grindstone [GRYND stohn] *n.* flat millstone for grinding grain into flour
    Dan always has his nose to the <u>grindstone</u>, working hard all the time.

impropriety [im pruh PRY i tee] *n.* improper action or behavior
    Margo's <u>impropriety</u> was that she never wrote thank-you notes.

neglected [ni GLEKT ed] *adj.* not properly cared for; ignored
    The <u>neglected</u> kitten badly needed warmth and food.

surviving [suhr VYV ing] *adj.* remaining alive; still living or existing
    The <u>surviving</u> spouse will continue to live in the house.

welfare [WEL fayr] *n.* well-being
    Bella was concerned about the <u>welfare</u> of her pet hamster.

Name _____ Date _____

A Christmas Carol: Scrooge and Marley, *Act I* by Israel Horovitz
Vocabulary Warm-up Exercises

Exercise A *Fill in each blank in the paragraph below with an appropriate word from Word List A. Use each word only once.*

Cindy liked to grow flowers, and her favorites were sunflowers that shone as bright

as [1] _____. To her, there was nothing else as pretty—they were

[2] _____! One day, Cindy's friend Michelle asked her if she could

have a sunflower for a bouquet. Cindy said no, and Michelle called her a greedy

[3] _____. "I hope each of your flowers dries up and

[4] _____!" said Michelle. Cindy immediately was sorry she had not

shared the flower with her friend. For her [5] _____ she put several

sunflowers in a [6] _____ copper vase. Marching to Michelle's house in

a [7] _____ way, Cindy apologized and gave the flowers to her friend.

Michelle smiled and offered to help Cindy plant more flowers to

[8] _____ her supply.

Exercise B *Find a **synonym** for each word in the following vocabulary list. Use each synonym in a sentence that makes the meaning of the word clear.*

Example: Vocabulary word: dismal   Synonym: *gloomy*
        Sample sentence: The gloomy dimness of the room was depressing.

1. establishments _____
   _____

2. welfare _____
   _____

3. impropriety _____
   _____

4. bleak _____
   _____

5. grindstone _____
   _____

6. surviving _____
   _____

7. neglected _____
   _____

A Christmas Carol: Scrooge and Marley, *Act I* by Israel Horovitz
Reading Warm-up A

Read the following passage. Pay special attention to the underlined words. Then, read it again, and complete the activities. Use a separate sheet of paper for your written answers.

This is the legend of King Midas, a greedy <u>miser</u> who hoarded all his valuables. It is said that more than anything, Midas loved shiny, yellow <u>gold</u>. This story tells how his love of it almost destroyed him.

Here is what happened. One day, King Midas met an important follower of the Greek god Dionysus. Midas let the man stay with him for a while, and then he guided the man back to Dionysus. Grateful for what he had done for his follower, the god told Midas he would grant him one wish.

At once, Midas requested that anything he touch be turned to gold. That ability would allow him to always <u>replenish</u> his supply of gold and to amass as large a fortune as he wanted. Dionysus granted the king's wish.

Midas immediately wanted to try it out, so on his way home he broke off a tree branch. It immediately turned to gold. "What <u>perfection</u>!" exclaimed Midas, admiring the brilliant, <u>lustrous</u> metal. He rejoiced, for now he would be the richest man on earth.

His happiness was not to last, however. For when he told his servants to bring a feast of celebration to him, he lifted a cup to drink. The cup and the liquid in it turned to gold. Next, he took a piece of bread. It, too, turned to gold. He suddenly realized that without food and drink, he could not live, just as a plant without sunlight <u>shrivels</u> and dies.

He began to realize that all his riches could not help him solve this dilemma. With a determined and <u>resolute</u> spirit, he prayed for Dionysus to undo the wish. He promised he would do whatever <u>penance</u> he could to make up for his greed. The god took pity on the king and told him how to undo the spell. From that day on, King Midas detested riches. He lived the rest of his life simply, enjoying what nature had to offer.

1. Circle the words that tell why Midas was a greedy <u>miser</u>. Use *miser* in a sentence.

2. Underline the words that describe how <u>gold</u> looks. What things might be made of *gold*?

3. Circle the words that tell what Midas wanted to <u>replenish</u>. Define *replenish*.

4. Underline the words that tell what was <u>perfection</u> to King Midas. What is *perfection* to you?

5. Circle the synonym for <u>lustrous</u>. Use *lustrous* in a sentence.

6. Underline the words that compare what happens to a plant that <u>shrivels</u> with what would happen to Midas. What does *shrivels* mean?

7. Underline the word that describes Midas's <u>resolute</u> spirit. Define *resolute*.

8. Circle the words that tell for what Midas promised to do <u>penance</u>. Why did he make that promise?

Name _____   Date _____

A Christmas Carol: Scrooge and Marley, *Act I* by Israel Horovitz
Reading Warm-up B

Read the following passage. Pay special attention to the underlined words. Then, read it again, and complete the activities. Use a separate sheet of paper for your written answers.

The Victorian Age in Britain was named after Queen Victoria. This era took place from the mid- to late 1800s. At that time, a great many children were not treated well. Poor children faced a <u>bleak</u>, hopeless future. They were sent to factories and other jobs to work long hours. Children whose families could afford to educate them might be sent away to boarding schools. Many of these <u>establishments</u> were run by strict and cruel headmasters, who regularly beat the students.

If a family was poor, or if one or both parents had died and the children were the <u>surviving</u> members of the family, the children were sent to work. Children earned less than adults, and their small hands were very nimble. These were two of the reasons that the owners of factories liked to hire children. Very little was done to safeguard the children's working conditions or <u>welfare</u> in these sweatshops. Children were often mangled by machinery. The shops were <u>dismal</u>, dirty places to work. The children toiled for long hours. They were powerless to rebel against these terrible conditions.

As a result of working long hours, always with their noses to the <u>grindstone</u>, the children and their families spent very little time together. Some children became servants in more wealthy households. The young servants had to follow many rules. It was an awful <u>impropriety</u> if they were seen or heard around the family for whom they worked.

Another common job for children was to become a chimney sweep. Again, their small size made them desirable for getting inside the chimneys to clean them. Burns, suffocation, and falls were common problems. Children were also used in the mines, where conditions were even worse, and many young workers perished.

The government and citizens of Victorian England badly <u>neglected</u> the basic needs of many children at work, school, and home.

1. Underline the word that is a synonym for <u>bleak</u>. What are some things you think are *bleak*?

2. Circle the words that tell what the <u>establishments</u> in the story are. Use *establishments* in a sentence.

3. Circle the words that tell more about what being <u>surviving</u> members of the family means. Define *surviving*.

4. Underline the words that give an example of how the <u>welfare</u> of the children was not safeguarded. What is *welfare*?

5. Underline the words that explain why the shops were <u>dismal</u>. Use *dismal* in a sentence.

6. Circle the words that tell why the children had their noses to the <u>grindstone</u>. Explain what this means.

7. Underline the words that tell what was an <u>impropriety</u>. Define *impropriety*.

8. Circle the words that tell what was <u>neglected</u> by people of Victorian England. What does *neglected* mean?

Name _____ Date _____

A Christmas Carol: Scrooge and Marley, Act I, by Israel Horovitz
Reading: Preview a Text to Set a Purpose for Reading

When you **set a purpose for reading,** you decide what you want to get from a text. Setting a purpose gives you a focus as you read. These are some of the reasons you might have for reading something:

- to learn about a subject
- to be entertained
- to gain understanding
- to prepare to take action or make a decision
- to find inspiration
- to complete a task

In order to set a purpose, **preview a text** before you read it. Look at the title, the pictures, the captions, the organization, and the beginnings of passages. If you already have a purpose in mind, previewing will help you decide whether the text will fit that purpose. If you do not have a purpose in mind, previewing the text will help you determine one.

DIRECTIONS: *Read the passages from Act I of* A Christmas Carol: Scrooge and Marley *indicated below, and then complete each item.*

1. Following the list of "The People of the Play," read the information labeled "The Place of the Play." Where is the play set?

   _____

2. Read the information labeled "The Time of the Play." When does the play take place?

   _____

3. What purpose or purposes might you set based on that information?

   _____

   _____

4. The illustrations that accompany the text of Act I of the play are photographs from a production of the play. Look at those photographs now, but ignore the one of the ghostly character in chains. How are the characters dressed?

   _____

5. Based on that information, what purpose might you set for reading Act I of the play?

   _____

6. Read the opening lines of Act I, Scene 1, spoken by a character called Marley. Then, look at the photograph of the ghostly character in chains. What purpose might you set based on that information?

   _____

Name _____ Date _____

A Christmas Carol: Scrooge and Marley, **Act I**, by Israel Horovitz
Literary Analysis: Dialogue

Dialogue is a conversation between characters. In a play, the characters are developed almost entirely through dialogue. Dialogue also advances the action of the plot and develops the conflict.

In the script of a dramatic work, you can tell which character is speaking by the name that appears before the character's lines. In this example of dialogue, you are introduced to two of the characters in *A Christmas Carol: Scrooge and Marley*:

NEPHEW. [*Cheerfully; surprising* SCROOGE] A merry Christmas to you, Uncle! God save you!

SCROOGE. Bah! Humbug!

NEPHEW. Christmas a "humbug," Uncle? I'm sure you don't mean that.

SCROOGE. I do! Merry Christmas? What right do you have to be merry? What reason have you to be merry? You're poor enough!

In just a few words apiece, the characters establish a conflict between them. The nephew thinks Christmas is a joyful holiday, and Scrooge thinks it is nonsense. This conflict will reappear throughout the play until it is resolved. Those lines of dialogue also give you a look at the character traits of Scrooge and his nephew. Scrooge is quarrelsome and unpleasant; the nephew is upbeat and friendly.

DIRECTIONS: *Answer the following questions about this passage from* A Christmas Carol: Scrooge and Marley, *Act I, Scene 2.*

PORTLY MAN. . . . [*Pen in hand; as well as notepad*] What shall I put you down for, sir?

SCROOGE. Nothing!

PORTLY MAN. You wish to be left anonymous?

SCROOGE. I wish to be left alone! [*Pauses; turns away; turns back to them*] Since you ask me what I wish, gentlemen, that is my answer. I help to support the establishments that I have mentioned; they cost enough: and those who are badly off must go there.

THIN MAN. Many can't go there; and many would rather die.

SCROOGE. If they would rather die, they had better do it, and decrease the surplus population. . . .

1. How many characters are speaking? Who are they?

_____

2. What is Scrooge like in this scene?

_____

3. How is he different from the men he is talking to?

_____

_____

4. Based on the identification of the characters, whom would you expect to speak next?

_____

Name _____ Date _____

A Christmas Carol: Scrooge and Marley, Act I, by Israel Horovitz
Vocabulary Builder

Word List

implored	morose	destitute	void	conveyed	benevolence

A. DIRECTIONS: *Think about the meaning of the italicized word from the Word List in each sentence. Then, answer the question, and explain your answer.*

1. Marley *implored* Scrooge to pay attention to him. Did Marley ask casually?

   _____

2. Scrooge was *morose*. Did he enjoy celebrating Christmas?

   _____

3. Are the *destitute* able to save money?

   _____

4. Scrooge looked into the *void*. Did he see anything?

   _____

5. In Act I, Scene 3, of *A Christmas Carol: Scrooge and Marley*, has Scrooge *conveyed* his fear?

   _____

6. Was Marley known for his *benevolence*?

   _____

B. DIRECTIONS: *For each item, write the letter of the word that means* the same or about the same as *the word from the Word List.*

____ 1. implored
      A. shouted   **B.** refused   **C.** begged   **D.** rejected

____ 2. morose
      A. cheerful   **B.** quarrelsome   **C.** sleepy   **D.** gloomy

____ 3. destitute
      A. poor   **B.** ill   **C.** rich   **D.** well

____ 4. void
      A. completion   **B.** remains   **C.** fullness   **D.** emptiness

____ 5. conveyed
      A. expressed   **B.** responded   **C.** activated   **D.** overcame

____ 6. benevolence
      A. indifference   **B.** remorse   **C.** kindness   **D.** happiness

Name _____ Date _____

A Christmas Carol: Scrooge and Marley, **Act I,** by Israel Horovitz
Support for Writing a Letter

Use this form to prepare to **write a letter** to Scrooge.

Salutation
State your main point: Scrooge is missing out in life by being cranky and negative with the people around him.

State a specific thing that Scrooge is missing out on. Include a detail from the play or from your experience to support your point.

State another specific thing that Scrooge is missing out on. Include a detail from the play or from your experience to support your point.

Conclude with a summary or a request that Scrooge change his behavior.

Closing,

Signature

Dear _____,

_____
_____
_____
_____
_____
_____
_____
_____
_____
_____
_____
_____
_____
_____
_____
_____
_____
_____
_____
_____
_____
_____
_____
_____
_____
_____
_____
_____
_____
_____

Now, prepare a final draft of your letter.

A Christmas Carol: Scrooge and Marley, **Act I,** by Israel Horovitz
Support for Extend Your Learning

Research and Technology

With the members of your group, consider the garments—the articles of clothing—that you must find out about in order to prepare **costume plans** for two characters in *A Christmas Carol: Scrooge and Marley.* You will most likely want to consider these items:

men's pants	men's vest	men's tie	women's dress
men's shirt	men's jacket	men's hat	women's hat

You might each choose two or three garments to research. Remember that you are researching the clothing that people of Scrooge's class would have worn in England in the 1840s. Enter the information on this chart.

Garment	Description of Garment, Including Type of Fabric and Color

Listening and Speaking

To prepare to give an **oral summary** of the plot of Act I of *A Christmas Carol: Scrooge and Marley,* complete this chart for the three major scenes:

Scene	Setting, Characters, Main Events, and Conflict
2	
3	
5	

Name _____ Date _____

A Christmas Carol: Scrooge and Marley, **Act I,** by Israel Horovitz
Enrichment: Social Services

In Act I of *A Christmas Carol: Scrooge and Marley,* two men visit Scrooge's office to collect money for the needy. Scrooge refers to prisons, workhouses, the treadmill, and the Poor Law—all of which were used in nineteenth-century England to deal with people who were poverty-stricken. In the United States more than 150 years after the events of *A Christmas Carol,* poverty is still a major problem. What do government and private agencies do today to try to help people in need?

A. DIRECTIONS: *Do research in a library, in a telephone directory, or on the Internet to find answers to the following questions.*

1. People whose earnings fall below the poverty line may be eligible to receive food stamps from the federal government. Where is the nearest office of the food-stamp agency in your area?

   _____

2. People in need may receive food, clothing, and shelter from organizations such as the Salvation Army. Where is the nearest Salvation Army center in your area? Where is the nearest soup kitchen? Is there another agency in your area that provides food, shelter, and clothing? If so, what is its name, and where is it located?

   _____

   _____

3. When people lose their home as a result of a fire, the American Red Cross often finds temporary shelter for them. Where is the nearest Red Cross office in your area?

   _____

4. Many senior citizens suffer from loneliness because they are unable to get around easily. Where is the nearest center providing services to senior citizens in your area?

   _____

5. Groups of people in communities often work together to help relieve the effects of poverty and hunger. Describe a group effort in your community. Who sponsors it? What is its mission?

   _____

B. DIRECTIONS: *Think about Ebenezer Scrooge's character in Act I of* A Christmas Carol: Scrooge and Marley *and his attitude toward people in need. Then, describe how you think Scrooge would react to one of the social services you learned about in doing your research for the first part of this activity. Would Scrooge be surprised by the service? Why or why not?*

_____

_____

A Christmas Carol: Scrooge and Marley, Act I, by Israel Horovitz
Build Language Skills: Vocabulary

Suffixes: -ment
The suffix -*ment* means "the act or quality of." Adding -*ment* to a verb creates a noun. *Pave* becomes *pavement*, "the quality of being paved; a paved surface." *Employ* becomes *employment*, "the act of being employed."

A. DIRECTIONS: *Add the suffix -*ment *to the italicized verb in each sentence. Then, write a new sentence using the noun you have created.*

1. The columns of text in the school newsletter did not *align*.

   _____

2. How would you *assess* the swimmer's chance of victory?

   _____

3. The witness will *state* her version of what occurred on the night of the crime.

   _____

4. Our principal will *announce* the winners of the spelling bee at tomorrow's assembly.

   _____

Academic Vocabulary Practice

B. DIRECTIONS: *Read each sentence, paying attention to the italicized Academic Vocabulary word. Indicate whether each statement is* true *or* false. *Then, explain your answer.*

1. A rousing cheer is a natural *reaction* to the loss of a championship game.

   T / F: _____ **Explanation:** _____

2. A teacher would be pleased to see her students' *involvement* with their schoolwork.

   T / F: _____ **Explanation:** _____

3. *Conflict* is the opposite of peacefulness.

   T / F: _____ **Explanation:** _____

4. You can get a good idea of a play by reading a *critique* of the production.

   T / F: _____ **Explanation:** _____

5. An *assumption* is the same as a certainty.

   T / F: _____ **Explanation:** _____

Name _____ Date _____

A Christmas Carol: Scrooge and Marley, **Act I,** by Israel Horovitz

Build Language Skills: Grammar

Interjections

An **interjection** is a part of speech that exclaims and expresses a feeling, such as pain or excitement. It may stand on its own, or it may appear within a sentence, but it functions independently of the sentence—it is not related to it grammatically. If an interjection stands on its own, it is set off with a period or an exclamation point. If it appears in a sentence, it is set off with commas.

Wow, look at that sunset!

My pants are covered with mud. Yuck!

Boy, do my legs ache after climbing all those stairs.

Here are some common interjections:

Boy	Hmmm	Oh	Ugh	Whew	Yikes
Hey	Huh	Oops	Well	Wow	Yuck

A. DIRECTIONS: *Rewrite each item. Punctuate the sentence or pair of sentences to set off the interjections. Some sentences or pairs of sentences may be written in more than one way.*

1. Oops the cat spilled his food all over the floor

   _____

2. Ouch I dropped the hammer on my foot

   _____

3. I worked for two hours in the hot sun Whew

   _____

4. Hmmm I think this CD costs way too much

   _____

5. Hey do not go near that downed electric wire

   _____

B. Writing Application: *Write three sentences using interjections. Be sure to punctuate the sentences correctly.*

1. _____

2. _____

3. _____

A Christmas Carol: Scrooge and Marley, *Act I,* by Israel Horovitz
Selection Test A

Critical Reading *Identify the letter of the choice that best answers the question.*

____ 1. In Act I, Scene 1, of *A Christmas Carol: Scrooge and Marley*, what purpose might you set after reading this passage, spoken by Marley?

> [*Cackle-voiced*] My name is Jacob Marley and I am dead. . . . Oh, no, there's no doubt that I am dead. The register of my burial was signed by the clergyman, the clerk, the undertaker . . . and by my chief mourner . . . Ebenezer Scrooge . . . I am dead as a doornail.

A. to complete a task
B. to take action or make a decision
C. to gain understanding of a character
D. to be inspired

____ 2. Suppose your purpose for reading *A Christmas Carol: Scrooge and Marley* was to understand how people spoke in England in the mid-1800s. Which part of the play would be most helpful?

A. the stage directions
B. the cast of characters
C. the dialogue
D. the captions

____ 3. Which purpose for reading might you set after previewing the photograph of Jacob Marley in Act I of *A Christmas Carol: Scrooge and Marley*?

A. to learn about a subject
B. to be entertained
C. to take action
D. to complete a task

____ 4. What do you learn about Scrooge from Jacob Marley in Act I, Scene 1, of *A Christmas Carol: Scrooge and Marley*?

A. He was a good friend to Marley.
B. He often gives money to the poor.
C. He is a solitary, miserly man.
D. He likes cold, dark winter days.

_____ 5. In Act I, Scene 2, of *A Christmas Carol: Scrooge and Marley,* what do you learn about the characters from the dialogue between Scrooge and his nephew?

A. They have different ideas about the worth of Christmas.

B. They have different ideas about the value of youth and age.

C. They have different ideas about how to run a business.

D. They have different ideas about the meaning of *humbug.*

_____ 6. What do you learn about Bob Cratchit from his dialogue with Scrooge in Act I, Scene 2, of *A Christmas Carol: Scrooge and Marley?*

A. He fears Scrooge and plans to find a new job.

B. He understands Scrooge and pities him.

C. He is angry with Scrooge and plans to get revenge.

D. He is poor and hopes Scrooge will pay him more.

_____ 7. In Act I, Scene 2, of *A Christmas Carol: Scrooge and Marley,* why does Scrooge object to people enjoying Christmas?

A. He is sad at Christmas because Marley died on Christmas Eve.

B. He actually likes Christmas and only pretends to dislike it.

C. He believes poor people should be unhappy even at Christmas.

D. He cares only for making money, and Christmas is an interruption.

_____ 8. When Scrooge goes home in Act I, Scene 3, which actions show that he is uneasy?

I. He trims his candle as he walks.

II. He checks each of the rooms.

III. He looks under the sofa and table.

IV. He sees Marley's face in the pictures.

A. I, II, IV

B. II, III, IV

C. I, II, III

D. I, III, IV

_____ 9. According to Act I, Scene 3, of *A Christmas Carol: Scrooge and Marley,* how did Marley get the chain that he wears?

A. It was given to him by the Ghost of Christmas Past.

B. It wrapped itself around him when he first screamed.

C. He created it to present to Scrooge as a gift.

D. He made it with his greed during his lifetime.

Name _____ Date _____

_____ 10. What is revealed about Scrooge's childhood in Act I, Scene 5?
  A. He was alone and lonely.
  B. He was his father's favorite.
  C. He cared only about money.
  D. He was afraid of ghosts.

_____ 11. According to the dialogue between the younger Scrooge and the woman in Act I, Scene 5, of *A Christmas Carol: Scrooge and Marley*, why is the woman ending their engagement?
  A. He is too interested in money.
  B. She thinks they are too young to marry.
  C. She believes he loves another woman.
  D. He calls her a mindless loon.

_____ 12. How is Marley different from the other characters in Act I of *A Christmas Carol: Scrooge and Marley*?
  A. He speaks directly to the audience.
  B. He is a ghost.
  C. He criticizes Scrooge's attitude.
  D. He is an apprentice.

Vocabulary and Grammar

_____ 13. In which of these lines is the meaning of the word *benevolence* best expressed?
  A. Many can't go there; and many would rather die.
  B. Oh, you'll be wanting the whole day tomorrow, I suppose?
  C. Whatever will it take to turn the faith of a miser from money to men?
  D. Father is so much kinder than he ever used to be.

_____ 14. Which of these lines contains an interjection?
  A. And it's cheaper than painting in a new sign, isn't it?
  B. What else can I be? Eh?
  C. But you don't keep it, Uncle.
  D. Merry Christmas to you sir, and a very, very happy New Year.

Essay

15. The conversation between Scrooge's nephew and Scrooge in Act I, Scene 2, of *A Christmas Carol: Scrooge and Marley* shows each character's ideas about Christmas. In a brief essay, summarize those ideas.

16. What evidence in Act I of *A Christmas Carol: Scrooge and Marley* suggests that Marley is the best person, or character, to try to change Scrooge's life? In an essay, explain your ideas. Cite two details from the play to support your points.

A Christmas Carol: Scrooge and Marley, *Act I*, by Israel Horovitz
Selection Test B

Critical Reading *Identify the letter of the choice that best completes the statement or answers the question.*

_____ 1. In Act I of *A Christmas Carol: Scrooge and Marley*, what purpose might you set for reading as you scan the list of "People in the Play" and see characters with such names as Portly Do-Gooder, The Ghost of Christmas Past, Fezziwig, and A Corpse?
A. to complete a task
B. to make a decision
C. to gain understanding
D. to be entertained

_____ 2. In Act I of *A Christmas Carol: Scrooge and Marley*, what purpose might you set after reading this opening passage, spoken by Scrooge?

They owe me money and I will collect. I will have them jailed, if I have to.

A. to be inspired
B. to gain understanding of a character
C. to take action or make a decision
D. to learn about a subject

_____ 3. Suppose your purpose for reading Act I of *A Christmas Carol: Scrooge and Marley* is to be entertained. Which elements of the text would contribute to that purpose?
A. the title
B. the captions
C. the photographs
D. the stage directions

_____ 4. What is the purpose of Marley's speech at the beginning of Act I, Scene 1, of *A Christmas Carol: Scrooge and Marley*?
A. to present himself as the Ghost of Christmas Past
B. to introduce the character of Scrooge to the audience
C. to explain why he and Scrooge were once partners
D. to tell Scrooge what to expect on Christmas Eve

_____ 5. Which line of dialogue best describes Scrooge's nephew's ideas about Christmas?
A. "Christmas a 'humbug,' Uncle? I'm sure you don't mean that."
B. "[Christmas is] when men and women seem to open their shut-up hearts freely."
C. "Don't be angry, Uncle. Come! Dine with us tomorrow."
D. "I'll keep my Christmas humor to the last. So a Merry Christmas, Uncle!"

____ 6. In Act I, what do you learn about Bob Cratchit from this dialogue?

NEPHEW. [*To* **CRATCHIT**] He's impossible!

CRATCHIT. Oh, mind him not, sir. He's getting on in years, and he's alone. He's noticed your visit. I'll wager your visit has warmed him.

A. He is angered by Scrooge.
B. He is forgiving of Scrooge.
C. He wishes he were Scrooge.
D. He agrees with Scrooge's nephew.

____ 7. Which of these lines, spoken by Scrooge in Act I of *A Christmas Carol: Scrooge and Marley*, reveals that Scrooge has a sense of humor?
A. "It's not convenient, and it's not fair."
B. "There's more of gravy than of grave about you."
C. "But why do spirits such as you walk the earth?"
D. "I cannot in any way afford to lose my days."

____ 8. In Act I, Scene 3, of *A Christmas Carol: Scrooge and Marley*, Scrooge does not believe that the vision he sees is in fact Marley. How does he express that doubt?
A. He says that he is seeing not Marley but a picture on the wall.
B. He says that someone is trying to frighten him or fool him.
C. He says that an undigested bit of food has affected his senses.
D. He says that someone who is dead could not appear before him.

____ 9. According to Marley in Act I, Scene 3, why does he walk the earth as a spirit?
A. He was unsuccessful in his lifetime.
B. He committed crimes in his lifetime.
C. He never did anything in his lifetime except make money.
D. He cheated Scrooge in his lifetime and now must repay him.

____ 10. In Act I, Scene 5, of *A Christmas Carol: Scrooge and Marley*, how does Scrooge respond to seeing the Christmas party of his former master, Fezziwig?
A. He thinks that he lavished too much praise on Fezziwig.
B. He realizes how much he has missed his sister, Fan.
C. He wishes he had given money to the boy singing carols.
D. He wishes he could say a word or two to Bob Cratchit.

____ 11. In the dialogue between young Scrooge and the woman in Act I, Scene 5, of *A Christmas Carol: Scrooge and Marley*, what does the woman say has replaced her in Scrooge's life?
A. another woman
B. his desire for wealth
C. his wish to travel
D. a new career

____ 12. The dialogue between young Scrooge and the woman in Act I, Scene 5, of *A Christmas Carol: Scrooge and Marley* advances the plot by showing the audience
   A. that Scrooge was once romantic.
   B. how Scrooge grew to be so alone.
   C. that the woman Scrooge loved was poor.
   D. how easily Scrooge can win arguments.

Vocabulary and Grammar

____ 13. In which of these lines is the meaning of the word *implored* best expressed?
   A. "Mr. Marley has been dead these seven years."
   B. "Bah! Humbug! Christmas! Bah! Humbug!"
   C. "But you were always a good man of business, Jacob."
   D. "No, Jacob! Don't leave me! I'm frightened!"

____ 14. In which of these lines is the meaning of the word *destitute* suggested?
   A. "Many thousands are in want of common necessities."
   B. "Oh, you'll be wanting the whole day tomorrow, I suppose?"
   C. "This is a game in which I lose my senses!"
   D. "Fly, but I am a mortal and cannot fly!"

____ 15. Which of these lines does *not* contain an interjection?
   A. "Oh, Schoolmaster. I'd like you to meet my little sister."
   B. "Uh, well, goodbye, Schoolmaster . . ."
   C. "Hilli-ho! Clear away, and let's have lots of room here!"
   D. "Even if I have grown so much wiser, what then?"

Essay

16. In Act I, Scene 5, of *A Christmas Carol: Scrooge and Marley,* when you learn what Scrooge was like when he was younger, do you feel more or less sympathy for him as an adult? In an essay, tell how Scrooge's experiences with the Ghost of Christmas Past make you feel about the Scrooge you see in Act I, Scene 2, of the play.

17. When Scrooge tells Marley that Marley was always "a good man of business," Marley responds:

> BUSINESS!!! Mankind was my business. The common welfare was my business; charity, mercy, forbearance, benevolence, were, all, my business.

In an essay, explain what you think Marley means by those words. Cite a detail about Marley that you have learned from the play to support your opinion.

A Christmas Carol: Scrooge and Marley, *Act II* by Israel Horovitz
Vocabulary Warm-up Word Lists

Study these words from the play. Then, complete the activities.

Word List A

fortune [FAWR chuhn] *n.* wealth, riches
   The rich woman owned a <u>fortune</u> in real estate.

heartily [HAHRT uh lee] *adv.* sincerely and fully
   Joe welcomed his friend <u>heartily</u> with a warm handshake.

poem [POH uhm] *n.* a written piece that presents a powerful image or feeling, sometimes in rhyming, rhythmic words
   Jane read the <u>poem</u> about spring aloud to the class.

praise [PRAYZ] *v.* to express approval or admiration
   Did the students applaud and <u>praise</u> Bob's performance?

recollect [rek uh LEKT] *v.* to remember
   I can <u>recollect</u> each time I spent the summer at the beach.

thoughtful [THAWT fuhl] *adj.* meditative or full of thought
   After watching the serious play, Dawn became quiet and <u>thoughtful</u>.

unaltered [un AWL tuhrd] *adj.* unchanged
   Her positive attitude toward running track remained <u>unaltered</u> by the long practice hours.

value [VAL yoo] *n.* the worth of a thing
   What is the <u>value</u> of this old watch?

Word List B

beggars [BEG uhrz] *n.* people who beg or ask for charity
   Some of the homeless people were <u>beggars</u>.

consequence [KAHN si kwuhns] *n.* a result of an action
   The <u>consequence</u> of preparing for the test will likely be a good grade.

nasty [NAS tee] *adj.* very ill-humored or unpleasant
   The <u>nasty</u> dog snarled at the baby.

odious [OH dee uhs] *adj.* arousing or deserving of hatred or disgust
   Tina disliked the <u>odious</u> smell of the garbage.

preserved [pree ZERVD] *v.* saved or maintained
   We <u>preserved</u> Grandma's wedding dress by carefully wrapping it up.

refuge [REF yooj] *n.* a safe place or shelter from danger
   The abandoned kitten found <u>refuge</u> with the little boy.

resource [REE sawrs] *n.* something that can be drawn upon if needed
   The backpackers carried extra food as a <u>resource</u> in case the hike took longer than expected.

workhouses [WERK how ziz] *n.* poorhouses
   Long ago, paupers in England were sent to live in <u>workhouses</u>.

Name _____ Date _____

A Christmas Carol: Scrooge and Marley, *Act II* by Israel Horovitz
Vocabulary Warm-up Exercises

Exercise A *Fill in each blank in the paragraph below with an appropriate word from Word List A. Use each word only once.*

I can still [1] _____ the way my friend Sharon looked when she

would write a(n) [2] _____. At such a time, she had a faraway,

[3] _____ expression on her face. Of course, neither of us knew then

that Sharon would become a famous writer and earn a(n) [4] _____. I

remember the first time she read one of her works aloud to an audience. The

people [5] _____ enjoyed the reading. People continue to

[6] _____ her work to this day. Sharon has remained

[7] _____ by fame. To her, the [8] _____ of the words she

writes is that she is able to share her feelings with her readers.

Exercise B *Decide whether each statement below is* true *or* false. *Explain your answers.*

1. <u>Beggars</u> usually do not have enough to eat.
   T / F _____

2. If a person is caught stealing by the police, there will be a negative <u>consequence</u> for the thief's action.
   T / F _____

3. If we <u>preserved</u> the old photos, then we threw them out.
   T / F _____

4. If Brenda likes the perfume, she thinks it has an <u>odious</u> aroma.
   T / F _____

5. Most people do not like to be told what to do in a <u>nasty</u> way.
   T / F _____

6. If people are sent to <u>workhouses</u>, that means they have a lot of money.
   T / F _____

7. If we have no <u>refuge</u> from the storm, we have nowhere to go.
   T / F _____

8. It's good to have extra office supplies as a <u>resource</u> when we do a big project, so we do not run out of paper.
   T / F _____

A Christmas Carol: Scrooge and Marley, *Act II* by Israel Horovitz
Reading Warm-up A

Read the following passage. Pay special attention to the underlined words. Then, read it again, and complete the activities. Use a separate sheet of paper for your written answers.

Ebenezer Scrooge is the main character of the story *A Christmas Carol* by Charles Dickens. Scrooge is known for his mean spirit and miserliness. In the story, he is visited by three ghosts on Christmas Eve. Scrooge decides to change after he begins to <u>recollect</u> his past and to think about his future.

Scrooge is an important character in literature. This is shown by the effect he has had on our culture. Although the original story was written in 1843, it still inspires us today. Scrooge's name has come to mean a stingy soul who has a <u>fortune</u> in money but is not rich in spirit. Many a <u>poem</u> has been written that mentions Scrooge. Songs also have been written about him. Plays and movies, as well as musicals, have been created to retell the story of Scrooge. Certain cartoon characters also bear his name. *Scrooge* can even be found in the dictionary, defined as "a miserly, hardened person."

An important part of the story of Scrooge is his ability to change into a better person. When he realizes that few will ever miss him because of the sort of life he has lived, he becomes <u>thoughtful</u>. He begs for a chance to change. Scrooge does not want his life to remain <u>unaltered</u>. When he awakens on Christmas morning, he is determined to become a better person. He <u>heartily</u> celebrates the day. He brings good humor to all and generosity to those in need. Scrooge proves by his actions that he knows the <u>value</u> of sharing with others. In turn, those who know him change their opinion of him. They <u>praise</u> his generous actions. The story of Scrooge, though written long ago, continues to entertain and to teach us.

1. Circle the words that tell what Scrooge begins to <u>recollect</u>. What is a synonym for *recollect*?

2. Underline the words that tell what kind of <u>fortune</u> Scrooge had. What kind of *fortune* didn't he have?

3. Circle the word that tells what many a <u>poem</u> has mentioned. What is a *poem*?

4. Underline the words that tell why Scrooge becomes <u>thoughtful</u>. Use *thoughtful* in a sentence.

5. Circle the word that is an antonym for <u>unaltered</u>. What is something you would like to remain *unaltered*?

6. Underline the sentence that tells how Scrooge <u>heartily</u> celebrates Christmas day. Define *heartily*.

7. Underline the words that tell of what Scrooge shows he knows the <u>value</u>. Of what do you know the *value*?

8. Circle the words that tell what people <u>praise</u>. What is an antonym of *praise*?

Name _____ Date _____

A Christmas Carol: Scrooge and Marley, *Act II* by Israel Horovitz
Reading Warm-up B

Read the following passage. Pay special attention to the underlined words. Then, read it again, and complete the activities. Use a separate sheet of paper for your written answers.

During the mid-1800s in England, the Industrial Revolution took place. The possibility of finding jobs in factories in London caused many people to move there. The city's population rose by 450 percent at this time. Although some profited by the Industrial Revolution, many did not. The lower class and lower middle class suffered much poverty. A <u>consequence</u> of the increased population was the growth of more slums. Orphans often became <u>beggars</u> because the government had no laws to protect them.

Factory workers also had no labor laws to protect them at first. They were paid low wages. They worked long hours under conditions that were <u>odious</u> and unclean. Young children and women were seen by factory owners as an inexpensive labor <u>resource</u>. This was because they could be paid lower wages than men. Later laws were passed that <u>preserved</u> the rights of children. Unfortunately, these laws were very hard to enforce.

People who could not pay their debts were sent to prison, where they were kept with criminals. Later changes in the law provided that the poor be sent to <u>workhouses</u>. There the inmates provided labor to pay for their food and shelter. The conditions in the workhouses were often quite <u>nasty</u>. Many poor did not find the workhouses to be a proper <u>refuge</u> to escape their poverty. They preferred homeless lives in the city, begging for charity in order to survive.

Some of the charities that were set up to help the poor failed. One provided wage supplements to laborers who did not have enough money for food. This plan backfired. Employers lowered the wages of many workers because they knew their employees would still be able to get food by using the supplements.

The Industrial Revolution in England, although it stimulated the economy, also brought with it serious social problems that needed to be solved.

1. Underline the words that tell what the <u>consequence</u> of the increased population was. Define **consequence**.

2. Circle the words that tell why some orphans became <u>beggars</u>. Use **beggars** in a sentence.

3. Circle the word that tells more about how the conditions were <u>odious</u>. What is a synonym for **odious**?

4. Underline the words that tell why employers thought of women and children as a cheap labor <u>resource</u>. What does **resource** mean?

5. Underline the words that tell what the later laws <u>preserved</u>. Use **preserved** in a sentence.

6. Circle the words that tell who was sent to the <u>workhouses</u>. Explain how the **workhouses** were different from the prisons.

7. Underline the words that tell what was <u>nasty</u>. What is something you think is **nasty**?

8. Circle the words that tell who did not think the workhouses were a proper <u>refuge</u>. Define **refuge**.

Name _____ Date _____

A Christmas Carol: Scrooge and Marley, *Act II,* by Israel Horovitz
Reading: Adjust Your Reading Rate to Suit Your Purpose

Setting a purpose for reading is deciding before you read what you want to get out of a text. The purpose you set will affect the way you read.

Adjust your reading rate to suit your purpose. When you read a play, follow these guidelines:

- Read stage directions slowly and carefully. They describe action that may not be revealed by the dialogue.
- Read short lines of dialogue quickly in order to create the feeling of conversation.
- Read longer speeches by a single character slowly in order to reflect on the character's words and look for clues to the message.

DIRECTIONS: *Read the following passages, and answer the questions that follow each one.*

MAN # 1. Hey, you, watch where you're going.

MAN # 2. Watch it yourself, mate!

[PRESENT *sprinkles them directly, they change.*]

MAN # 1. I pray go in ahead of me. It's Christmas. You be first!

MAN # 2. No, no. I must insist that YOU be first!

1. How would you read the preceding dialogue? Why?

   _____

2. How would you read the stage directions? Why?

   _____

3. What important information do the stage directions contain? How does it affect your understanding of the lines that follow it?

   _____

   _____

PRESENT. Mark my words, Ebenezer Scrooge. I do not present the Cratchits to you because they are a handsome, or brilliant family. They are not handsome. They are not brilliant. They are not well-dressed, or tasteful to the times. Their shoes are not even waterproofed by virtue of money or cleverness spent. So when the pavement is wet, so are the insides of their shoes and the tops of their toes. They are the Cratchits, Mr. Scrooge. They are not highly special. They are happy, grateful, pleased with one another, contented with the time and how it passes. They don't sing very well, do they? But, nonetheless, they do sing . . . [*Pauses*] think of that, Scrooge. Fifteen shillings a week and they do sing . . . hear their song until its end.

4. How would you read the preceding passage? Why?

   _____

   _____

Name _____   Date _____

A Christmas Carol: Scrooge and Marley, *Act II*, by Israel Horovitz
Literary Analysis: Stage Directions

Stage directions are the words in the script of a drama that are not spoken by characters. When a play is performed, you can see the set, the characters, and the movements, and you can hear the sound effects. When you read a play, you get this information from the stage directions. Stage directions are usually printed in italic type and set off by brackets or parentheses.

DIRECTIONS: *Read the following passages, and answer the questions that follow each one.*

[BOB CRATCHIT *enters, carrying* TINY TIM *atop his shoulder. He wears a threadbare and fringeless comforter hanging down in front of him.* TINY TIM *carries small crutches and his small legs are bound in an iron frame brace.*]

1. Who appears in this scene?

    _____

2. What does the description of Bob Cratchit reveal about the Cratchit family?

    _____

3. What does the description of Tiny Tim reveal about him?

    _____

    _____

SCROOGE. Specter, something informs me that our parting moment is at hand. I know it, but I know not how I know it.

[FUTURE *points to the other side of the stage. Lights out on* CRATCHITS. FUTURE *moves slowing, gliding . . .* FUTURE *points opposite.* FUTURE *leads* SCROOGE *to a wall and a tombstone. He points to the stone.*]

Am *I* that man those ghoulish parasites so gloated over?

4. Who appears in this scene? How do you know?

    _____

    _____

5. What do the stage directions reveal that the dialogue does not reveal?

    _____

    _____

    _____

Name _____ Date _____

A Christmas Carol: Scrooge and Marley, *Act II,* by Israel Horovitz
Vocabulary Builder

Word List

astonish   compulsion   severe   meager   audible

A. DIRECTIONS: *Think about the meaning of the italicized word from the Word List in each sentence. Then, answer the question, and explain your answer.*

1. Scrooge's new attitude will *astonish* his family. Will they be surprised by it?
   _____

2. Scrooge has a *compulsion* to go with each of the ghosts. Can he easily resist going?
   _____

3. Mrs. Cratchit's judgment of Scrooge is *severe.* Does she think highly of him?
   _____

4. Scrooge paid Cratchit a *meager* salary. Was the salary generous?
   _____

5. The actor's voice is *audible* when he whispers. Can the audience hear him?
   _____

B. DIRECTIONS: *Write the letter of the word whose meaning is* the same or about the same as *the meaning of the word from the Word List.*

___ 1. astonish
   A. frighten   B. puzzle   C. amaze   D. question

___ 2. compulsion
   A. rejection   B. desire   C. expectation   D. need

___ 3. severe
   A. mild   B. tall   C. fast   D. harsh

___ 4. meager
   A. insufficient   B. nonsensical   C. mistaken   D. required

___ 5. audible
   A. loud   B. visible   C. hidden   D. silent

Name _____ Date _____

A Christmas Carol: Scrooge and Marley, *Act II,* by Israel Horovitz
Support for Writing a Tribute

To prepare to write a **tribute,** or expression of admiration, to the changed Ebenezer Scrooge, answer the following questions.

What is Scrooge like before the change?

_____

_____

What anecdotes—brief stories that make a point—illustrate Scrooge's character before the change?

_____

_____

_____

_____

What causes Scrooge to change?

_____

_____

_____

What is Scrooge like after the change?

_____

_____

What anecdotes illustrate Scrooge's character after the change?

_____

_____

_____

_____

Now, write a draft of your tribute to Scrooge. Be sure to explain how Scrooge has changed and why his new behavior deserves to be honored. Use this space to write your first draft.

_____

_____

_____

_____

Name _____   Date _____

A Christmas Carol: Scrooge and Marley, *Act II,* by Israel Horovitz
Support for Extend Your Learning

Research and Technology

Use the following chart to gather information for a **timeline** of the life of Charles Dickens. Focus on the major events in Dickens's life, the serialization of his most important literary works, and his travels and speaking engagements. See whether you can find an event for each date listed below. Include additional dates if you wish.

Timeline of the Life and Works of Charles Dickens

1812:	
1824:	
1836:	
1837:	
1842:	
1843:	
1849:	
1858:	
1859:	
1860:	
1868:	
1870:	

Listening and Speaking

You must base your **dramatic monologue** on Scrooge's thoughts as he interacts with the Ghost of Christmas Present or the Ghost of Christmas Past. As you prepare your monologue, answer these questions:

On which scene and with which ghost will you focus your monologue? (Be specific.)

_____

What is happening in this scene? _____

_____

What is Scrooge feeling in this scene? Is he excited, eager, anxious, frightened?

_____

Now, write a draft of your monologue. Remember to speak as if you were Scrooge: Use the pronouns *I, me, my, mine,* and *myself.* Practice presenting the monologue, and then revise your draft to correct any weaknesses you notice.

Name _____ Date _____

A Christmas Carol: Scrooge and Marley, *Act II,* by Israel Horovitz
Enrichment: Holiday Observances

In Act II of *A Christmas Carol: Scrooge and Marley,* Scrooge observes how the Cratchits celebrate Christmas. Later in the play, he contributes to the Cratchits' celebration by sending the family a turkey, and he joins his nephew's family as they celebrate the holiday.

You and your family may observe and celebrate holidays throughout the year in special ways. Traditions may include festive meals, gift-giving, dressing in special clothing, visiting friends and relatives, or visiting special places.

A. DIRECTIONS: *Think of a holiday that is widely celebrated or observed. Think about all the special ways in which you, your family, and/or other people mark this occasion. Fill in details about the holiday observance.*

1. Name of holiday: _____
2. Meaning of holiday: _____
   _____
   _____
3. Clothing typically worn on holiday: _____
   _____
4. Special foods eaten on this holiday: _____
   _____
5. Places visited on this holiday: _____
   _____
6. Activities engaged in on this holiday: _____
   _____
7. Other traditions associated with this holiday: _____
   _____

B. DIRECTIONS: *Imagine that you could establish a new holiday. It might be serious (Help the Homeless Day) or lighthearted (Backwards Day). Answer these questions about your holiday:*

1. What is its name? _____
2. What is its purpose? _____
   _____
3. What traditions will your holiday involve? _____
   _____

A Christmas Carol: Scrooge and Marley, *Act II,* by Israel Horovitz
Build Language Skills: Vocabulary

Suffixes: *-tion*

The suffix *-tion* creates a noun that names the quality, act, or result of the word to which it is added. When you add *-tion* to the verb *react,* for example, you create the noun *reaction,* which means "the act of reacting." When you add *-tion* to the verb *assume,* you create the noun *assumption,* which means "the act of assuming or taking for granted."

A. DIRECTIONS: *Add the suffix -tion to the italicized verb in each sentence. Then, write a new sentence using the noun you have created.*

1. When I was younger, I had difficulty with problems that ask you to *subtract.*
   _____

2. Will the stores *reduce* their prices after the holidays?
   _____

3. Do not *assume* that the weather will remain sunny all day.
   _____

4. Do you have a device that can *detect* carbon monoxide in your home?
   _____

5. Can the team afford to *add* new uniforms to its budget?
   _____

Academic Vocabulary Practice

B. DIRECTIONS: *Read each sentence, paying attention to the italicized Academic Vocabulary word. Then, revise the sentence so that the vocabulary word is used logically. Be sure to use the vocabulary word in your revised sentence.*

1. I knew I had no *reaction* to the scary movie because after I saw it, I had nightmares.
   _____

2. The philanthropist's lack of interest in the project was evidence of his *involvement* in it.
   _____

3. The two characters' friendliness to each other was proof of their *conflict.*
   _____

4. Before the critic saw the play, she wrote a *critique* predicting that it would succeed.
   _____

5. Because we were sure of all the facts about Dickens's life, we made an *assumption* about the writer's character.
   _____

A Christmas Carol: Scrooge and Marley, *Act II,* by Israel Horovitz
Build Language Skills: Grammar

Double Negatives

Double negatives occur when two negative words appear in a sentence but only one is needed. Examples of negative words are *nothing, not, never,* and *no.* You can correct a double negative by revising the sentence.

Incorrect	**Correct**
I do <u>not</u> have <u>no</u> homework tonight.	I do <u>not</u> have <u>any</u> homework tonight.
You <u>never</u> said <u>nothing</u> about that movie.	You <u>never</u> said <u>anything</u> about that movie.

A. DIRECTIONS: *Put a checkmark (✓) next to each sentence that uses a negative word correctly. Put an ✗ next to each sentence that contains a double negative.*

____ 1. Do not ever say nothing to Mom about the surprise party.

____ 2. You never told me anything about your new coach.

____ 3. The team never had time to make a comeback.

____ 4. We do not have no reason to get up early tomorrow.

____ 5. They did not have no money for the movie.

B. Writing Application: *Rewrite each sentence to eliminate the double negative.*

1. We do not have no bread for sandwiches.

   _____

2. The spy never had no intention of giving himself up.

   _____

3. This article does not have nothing to do with our assignment.

   _____

4. They are not going to no championship game tonight.

   _____

5. Our dog will not ever eat no food she does not like.

   _____

A Christmas Carol: Scrooge and Marley, *Act II*, by Israel Horovitz
Selection Test A

Critical Reading *Identify the letter of the choice that best answers the question.*

____ 1. What is mainly described in this passage from Act II, Scene 1, of *A Christmas Carol: Scrooge and Marley*?

> [PRESENT *is wearing a simple green robe. The walls around the room are now covered in greenery, as well. The room seems to be a perfect grove now: leaves of holly, mistletoe and ivy reflect the stage lights. Suddenly, there is a mighty roar of flame in the fireplace and now the hearth burns with a lavish, warming fire.*]

> A. the Ghost's size
> B. the Ghost's room
> C. the Ghost's attitude
> D. the Ghost's orchard

____ 2. When he meets the Ghost of Christmas Present in Act II, Scene 1, what does Scrooge say that shows he has already changed?
> A. "Come in, come in! Come in and know me better!"
> B. "Have you had many brothers, Spirit?"
> C. "A tremendous family to provide for!"
> D. "If you have aught to teach me, let me profit by it."

____ 3. What element of drama is shown in this excerpt from *A Christmas Carol: Scrooge and Marley*, Act II, Scene 1?

> [SCROOGE *walks cautiously to* PRESENT *and touches his robe. When he does, lightning flashes, thunder claps, music plays. Blackout*]

> A. dialogue
> B. plot
> C. stage directions
> D. setting

____ 4. What do you learn about Scrooge from this passage from Act II, Scene 3?

> **PRESENT.** This is the home of your employee, Mr. Scrooge. Don't you know it?
> **SCROOGE.** Do you mean Cratchit, Spirit? Do you mean this is Cratchit's home?

> A. He has a poor memory for places.
> B. He has forgotten his employee's name.
> C. He has never visited the Cratchits' home.
> D. He is trying to annoy the Ghost.

_____ 5. In Act II, Scene 3, of *A Christmas Carol: Scrooge and Marley*, what is Scrooge's first reaction on seeing Cratchit's family?

   A. He thinks Cratchit has too many children.

   B. He is afraid that Tiny Tim will not live.

   C. He is touched that Cratchit toasts him.

   D. He wants to think about what he sees.

_____ 6. In Act II, Scene 3, of *A Christmas Carol: Scrooge and Marley*, what does Christmas Present say to indicate that Scrooge's actions can affect the outcome of events?

   A. "I would say that he gets the pleasure of his family."

   B. "I see a vacant seat . . . in the poor chimney corner, and a crutch without an owner."

   C. "If these shadows remain unaltered by the future, the child will die."

   D. "Save your breath, Mr. Scrooge. You can't be seen or heard."

_____ 7. If you were to adjust your reading rate to suit your purpose, how would you read this passage from *A Christmas Carol: Scrooge and Marley*, Act II, Scene 3?

   MRS. CRATCHIT. And how did little Tim behave?

   BOB. As good as gold, and even better. Somehow he gets thoughtful sitting by himself so much, and thinks the strangest things you ever heard. He told me, coming home, that he hoped people saw him in the church, because he was a cripple, and it might be pleasant to them to remember upon Christmas Day, who made lame beggars walk and blind men see. . . . He has the oddest ideas sometimes, but he seems all the while to be growing stronger and more hearty . . . one would never know.

   A. slowly, to look for clues to the message

   B. quickly, to create a feeling of conversation

   C. quickly, to pass over unimportant information

   D. slowly, to look for information not in the dialogue

_____ 8. In Act II, Scene 4, of *A Christmas Carol: Scrooge and Marley*, what are the two women and the man selling to Old Joe?

   A. items they stole from Scrooge's rooms after he died

   B. items Scrooge gave them before he died

   C. items Cratchit gave them after Scrooge died

   D. items Scrooge kept to remind himself of his first love

_____ 9. In Act II, Scene 4, of *A Christmas Carol: Scrooge and Marley*, what does the Ghost of Christmas Future do that gives Scrooge hope?

   A. He never speaks a word to Scrooge.

   B. He points to Scrooge's tombstone.

   C. He pulls away from Scrooge.

   D. He drops his garments and disappears.

____ **10.** If you were adjusting your reading rate to suit your purpose, how would you read this passage from Act II, Scene 5?

> **SCROOGE.** . . . I am light as a feather, I am happy as an angel, I am as merry as a schoolboy. [*Yells out window and then out to audience*] Merry Christmas to everybody! Merry Christmas to everybody! A Happy New Year to all the world! Hallo there! Whoop! Whoop! Hallo! Hallo!

    A. slowly and carefully

    B. quickly, to create the feeling of conversation

    C. quickly, skipping the stage directions

    D. slowly, to look for clues to the message

Vocabulary and Grammar

____ **11.** In which line is the opposite of the word *audible* best expressed?

    A. "Spirit, tell me if Tiny Tim will live."

    B. "Save your breath, Mr. Scrooge. You can't be . . . heard."

    C. "I'll drink to his health for your sake . . ., but not for his sake."

    D. "Mark my words, Ebenezer Scrooge."

____ **12.** Which of the following sentences contains a double negative?

    A. No one is as dearly loved as Tiny Tim.

    B. The man does not know much about Scrooge's death.

    C. Scrooge declares that he is not the man he was.

    D. Scrooge realizes that he has not missed nothing.

Essay

13. In Act II of *A Christmas Carol: Scrooge and Marley,* Scrooge visits the homes of the Cratchits and his nephew, Fred, with the Ghost of Christmas Present. In an essay, describe what those two visits have in common and what Scrooge learns from them.

14. Why is the Ghost of Christmas Future the most frightening of the three ghosts in *A Christmas Carol: Scrooge and Marley*? In an essay, explain what is frightening about this character. Cite two details from the play to support your points.

A Christmas Carol: Scrooge and Marley, *Act II,* by Israel Horovitz
Selection Test B

Critical Reading *Identify the letter of the choice that best completes the statement or answers the question.*

____ 1. In Act II, Scene 1, of *A Christmas Carol: Scrooge and Marley*, Marley says that nothing will astonish Scrooge now and so he will give him nothing. What does he mean by that?
   A. He wants to drive Scrooge crazy.
   B. He is making a play on the word *nothing*.
   C. He has used all his magic tricks in the first act.
   D. He is afraid Scrooge will discover how he does his magic.

____ 2. What is the most important information the reader gets from these stage directions in Act II, Scene 1, of *A Christmas Carol: Scrooge and Marley*?
   [*Heaped up on the floor, to form a kind of throne, are turkeys, geese, game, poultry, brawn, great joints of meat, . . . mince-pies, plum puddings, . . . cherry-cheeked apples, juicy oranges, luscious pears, . . . and seething bowls of punch, that make the chamber dim with their delicious steam. Upon this throne sits* PRESENT, *glorious to see.*]

   A. how the Ghost of Christmas Present looks
   B. how the Ghost of Christmas Present spends his time
   C. what foods wealthy people ate in nineteenth-century England
   D. how a room full of food and drink might look and smell

____ 3. What does the playwright most likely mean to suggest at the end of these stage directions from Act II, Scene 2, of *A Christmas Carol: Scrooge and Marley*?
   [*The choral groups will hum the song they have just completed now and mill about the streets, carrying their dinners to the bakers' shops and restaurants. They will, perhaps, sing about being poor at Christmastime, whatever.*]

   A. The chorus should continue singing and carrying food.
   B. The chorus members should be grouped together on the stage.
   C. The director should decide what the chorus will sing about.
   D. The bakers' shops and the restaurants should be open for business.

____ 4. If you were to adjust your reading rate to suit your purpose, how would you best read this passage from Act II, Scene 3, of *A Christmas Carol: Scrooge and Marley*?
   SCROOGE. What is this place, Spirit?
   PRESENT. This is the home of your employee, Mr. Scrooge. Don't you know it?
   SCROOGE. Do you mean Cratchit, Spirit? Do you mean this is Cratchit's home?

   A. slowly, to look for clues to the message
   B. quickly, to create a feeling of conversation
   C. quickly, to get a general sense of the conversation
   D. slowly, to look for information that is not stated directly

Name _____ Date _____

_____ 5. What purpose is served by these stage directions, from Act II, Scene 3?

[SCROOGE *touches* PRESENT'S *robe. The lights fade out on the* CRATCHITS, *who sit, frozen, at the table.* SCROOGE *and* PRESENT *in a spotlight now. Thunder, lightning, smoke. They are gone.*]

A. They explain Scrooge's character.
B. They signal a change of setting.
C. They describe the Cratchit home.
D. They show the director's skill.

_____ 6. What aspect of this passage, from Act II, Scene 4, of *A Christmas Carol: Scrooge and Marley*, signals that it should be read slowly?

PRESENT. They are Man's children, and they cling to me, appealing from their fathers. The boy is Ignorance; the girl is Want. Beware them both, and all of their degree, but most of all beware this boy, for I see that written on his brow which is doom, unless the writing be erased.

A. It takes place in Act II of the play.
B. It contains no stage directions.
C. It is a longer speech by one character.
D. It is conversational in tone.

_____ 7. According to Act II, Scene 4, of *A Christmas Carol: Scrooge and Marley*, why does Fred intend to invite Scrooge to Christmas dinner every year?
A. Scrooge reminds Fred of his mother, Scrooge's sister.
B. Fred likes to tease Scrooge and make him angry.
C. Fred and his wife enjoy laughing at their miserly uncle.
D. Fred wants Scrooge to see how meager their Christmas is.

_____ 8. What does Scrooge mean by this line from Act II, Scene 4?

Spirit, this is a fearful place. In leaving it, I shall not leave its lesson, trust me. Let us go!

A. I am afraid and want us to leave.
B. This is not a good place for a school.
C. I will not forget the lesson I learned here.
D. If you do not trust me, I will not follow you.

_____ 9. Why do the scoundrels in Act II, Scene 4, of *A Christmas Carol: Scrooge and Marley* have access to Scrooge's possessions?
A. Scrooge died alone with no one to take care of his things.
B. Scrooge left his things to anyone who might need them.
C. Scrooge did not get around to making a will before he died.
D. Scrooge left his door unlocked on the last night he was alive.

_____ 10. Which line spoken by Marley in Act II of *A Christmas Carol: Scrooge and Marley* best summarizes the theme of the play?
A. "The firm of Scrooge and Marley is doubly blessed."
B. "Yes, Ebenezer, the bedpost is your own. Believe it!"
C. "Scrooge was better than his word. He did it all and infinitely more."
D. "And it was always said of him that he knew how to keep Christmas well."

Vocabulary and Grammar

___ 11. In which line is the meaning of the word *astonish* expressed?
A. Marley says that nothing will surprise Scrooge, given all that he has seen.
B. Christmas Present asks Scrooge whether he has ever before seen anyone like him.
C. Fred's wife expresses her pleasure at the amount of laughter in her marriage.
D. Bob Cratchit requests that Martha play the notes on the lute for Tiny Tim's song.

___ 12. In which sentence is the meaning of the word *severe* expressed?
A. On Christmas Day, the streets are full of people going to work in the homes of the rich.
B. Christmas Present seems to scold Scrooge for not recognizing the Cratchits' home.
C. Scrooge wonders aloud whether he can affect the events of the future.
D. When the weather is harsh, people make music to lift their spirits.

___ 13. Which sentence does *not* contain a double negative?
A. Mrs. Cratchit does not want to make no toast to Scrooge.
B. No one says nothing about the cause of Scrooge's death.
C. Cratchit says they will not never quarrel among themselves.
D. Scrooge seems to want to know nothing about his death.

Essay

14. Act II of *A Christmas Carol: Scrooge and Marley* contains several messages. In an essay, tell how one of these messages is conveyed in the second act of the play:

- When one person changes for the better, others are affected for the better.
- Only greedy people will be present at the end of a greedy life.
- Wealth makes people rich only if they share their wealth.

Include at least two details from the play to support your points.

15. Tiny Tim's character is revealed through stage directions and dialogue. In an essay, describe the boy based on what you learn in Act II of *A Christmas Carol: Scrooge and Marley.* Tell what he looks like, how he feels about his family, and any other information about him that is revealed in the text you read. If Tiny Tim could be said to represent a single characteristic, what would it be?

Vocabulary Warm-up Word Lists

Study these words from the play. Then, complete the activities.

Word List A

absolute [AB suh loot] *adj.* complete or whole
After the stirring speech, there was <u>absolute</u> silence.

compete [kuhm PEET] *v.* to contend or to vie for something
The county ski teams will <u>compete</u> for a downhill racing prize.

enormously [ee NOOR muhs lee] *adv.* immensely
The <u>enormously</u> big wedding cake took up the whole table.

faintly [FAYNT lee] *adv.* weakly or slightly
Anna <u>faintly</u> heard a noise outside the door.

feast [FEEST] *n.* big, festive meal
We ate a huge <u>feast</u> at the anniversary party.

grace [GRAYS] *n.* sense of what is right, proper, and decent
The host greeted his guests with a welcome that was full of <u>grace</u>.

gratitude [GRAT i tood] *n.* thankfulness
The winning team felt a sense of <u>gratitude</u> for their coach.

suitors [SOOT erz] *n.* men who are courting a woman
Linda's <u>suitors</u> called her each day.

Word List B

apprentices [uh PREN tis iz] *n.* people who work to learn a trade from an expert
The silversmith's <u>apprentices</u> were eager to learn how to work with metal.

attention [uh TEN shuhn] *n.* the state of standing tall, awaiting an order or instruction
The soldiers stood at <u>attention</u> when the commander entered the room.

bound [BOWND] *adv.* certain, sure, or having one's mind made up
We are <u>bound</u> to win this tournament.

convenient [kuhn VEEN yuhnt] *adj.* causing little trouble or work
Will it be <u>convenient</u> for you if we meet at eight o'clock?

dignity [DIG ni tee] *n.* the quality of being worthy of honor or respect
Susan had a lot of <u>dignity</u> when she addressed the court.

master [MAS ter] *n.* boss or person in charge
The <u>master</u> of the shop told his employees to be on time.

snuffs [SNUHFS] *v.* puts out a candle or extinguishes something
The priest <u>snuffs</u> out the candles after the service.

wages [WAYJ iz] *n.* pay
Dan spent his week's <u>wages</u> on repairing his car.

from A Christmas Carol: Scrooge and Marley, *Act I, Scenes 2 & 5* by Israel Horovitz
Vocabulary Warm-up Exercises

Exercise A *Fill in each blank in the paragraph below with an appropriate word from Word List A. Use each word only once.*

Rachel was a very nice person and was [1] _____ popular with her class-mates. At the holiday [2] _____ at school, aside from lots of food, there was also music for dancing. Rachel had many [3] _____. Each wished to [4] _____ for a chance to dance with Rachel. She responded to each one with complete and [5] _____ politeness. Her thankfulness was not [6] _____ expressed. Instead, she treated her admirers with dignified [7] _____, showing [8] _____ for each invitation she received.

Exercise B *Answer the questions with complete sentences.*

1. Would <u>apprentices</u> be likely to earn a lot of money?

   _____

2. If it is <u>convenient</u> to get to work, does it take an extremely long time?

   _____

3. If we are <u>bound</u> to run into a snowstorm, should we allow some extra travel time?

   _____

4. When someone stands at <u>attention</u>, is he or she likely to be a member of the armed forces?

   _____

5. Do most people dislike being treated with <u>dignity</u>?

   _____

6. If the craftsperson is a <u>master</u> at woodworking, is she or he probably just learning that trade?

   _____

7. If the girl <u>snuffs</u> out the flame, will the room probably grow darker?

   _____

8. Will a person be likely to earn more <u>wages</u> if he or she spends more time working?

   _____

from **A Christmas Carol: Scrooge and Marley,** *Act I, Scenes 2 & 5* by Israel Horovitz
Reading Warm-up A

Read the following passage. Pay special attention to the underlined words. Then, read it again, and complete the activities. Use a separate sheet of paper for your written answers.

December 22, 1843

Dear Diary,

Today was a wonderful day! My family and I went to my Aunt Annie's for a holiday party. It was an <u>absolute</u> success! Cousin Mary played the piano as we danced to her lively tunes. Some dancers moved with a sense of <u>grace</u>, while others, such as my brothers, tried to <u>compete</u> with each other to see how many high kicks, fancy steps, and turns they could do!

My older sister Julianne had many <u>suitors</u>. They stood by her side as they awaited a turn to dance with her. I noticed she did not go anywhere near the kissing ball, which was hanging from the ceiling of the room. It was filled with mistletoe and other evergreens. Everyone knows that if you are found beneath it, you must kiss someone.

We enjoyed a fine <u>feast</u> of goose and beef. The tasty treats were <u>enormously</u> popular with all. On Christmas, I look forward to more holiday foods, for that is when we will eat our delicious plum pudding. It is made of prunes, raisins, and beef. Sweet mince pies will also be served. They are made of spices, fruit, and mincemeat. We will eat them throughout the twelve days of Christmas in order to bring us twelve months of good luck in the coming year.

Aunt Annie's house looked lovely. It was decorated with fresh evergreen boughs, which are thought to bring good luck and to represent renewed life. The entire family sang carols, and it was not <u>faintly</u> done. I believe our booming voices could be heard near and far.

I was sad to see the evening come to an end, for it was such fun. I hugged my aunt, expressing my <u>gratitude</u> for having such a fine family with whom to celebrate! Well, that is all for tonight.

Nora

1. Circle the words that tell what was an <u>absolute</u> success. What does *absolute* mean?

2. Underline the words that tell who moved with <u>grace</u>. Use *grace* in a sentence.

3. Circle the words that describe how Nora's brothers tried to <u>compete</u>. What other things can people *compete* in?

4. Underline the words that tell what Julianne's <u>suitors</u> did. Define *suitors*.

5. Circle the words that tell of what the <u>feast</u> consisted. To you, what foods make up a *feast*?

6. Underline the words that tell what was <u>enormously</u> popular. What is a synonym for *enormously*?

7. Underline the words that tell what was not <u>faintly</u> done. Describe how it must have sounded.

8. Circle the words that tell for what Nora was expressing her <u>gratitude</u>. Define *gratitude*.

from **A Christmas Carol: Scrooge and Marley,** *Act I,* **Scenes 2 & 5** by Israel Horovitz
Reading Warm-up B

Read the following passage. Pay special attention to the underlined words. Then, read it again, and complete the activities. Use a separate sheet of paper for your written answers.

The Victorian age in Britain was named after the ruling queen of the time, Victoria. It took place during the 1800s. At that time, families who could not pay their debts were sent to places called workhouses.

The children in workhouses were often given jobs to help pay off their families' debts. Factory owners and craftspeople looking for cheap labor knew they were <u>bound</u> to find such workers among poor children. Such employers found it <u>convenient</u> to ask the workhouses to give them youngsters as <u>apprentices</u>.

If a child became an apprentice, he or she would learn a trade, such as blacksmith or glass blower. The child would be given room and board in exchange for working for a <u>master</u>, the owner or boss of the shop. If a child was being apprenticed, indenture papers were drawn up. These papers were a contract between the master and the apprentice. It listed the conditions under which the apprentice would work. It also told how long the arrangement would last. One such contract describes the apprenticeship of a boy of thirteen who was sent to work with a shoemaker for seven years. The boy would not receive any pay, or <u>wages</u>, for the first four years. Every year after that he would receive a small amount of money.

Some masters were kind and treated the young workers with respect and <u>dignity</u>. Others saw the youngsters as slaves. These apprentices needed always to be at <u>attention</u>, ready to perform the next task required of them. In such cases, the youngsters' spirit was extinguished, just as one <u>snuffs</u> out a candle's flame.

Some workhouses looked into the conditions that the children would be working under during their apprenticeships. They wanted to make sure that the work was not too difficult and that the youngsters would be treated well. Unfortunately, those workhouses were the exception, not the rule. Thus, the lives of many young apprentices were not easy.

1. Underline the words that tell what the factory owners and craftspeople were <u>bound</u> to find among the poor children. Define *bound*.

2. Circle the words that tell what the employers found to be <u>convenient</u>. Use *convenient* in a sentence.

3. Circle the sentences that define what <u>apprentices</u> are. If you were an *apprentice*, what craft would you like to learn to do?

4. Underline the words that tell what a <u>master</u> is. Use *master* in a sentence.

5. Underline the word that is a synonym for <u>wages</u>. Do you think it was fair that the boy would receive no *wages* for the first four years?

6. Circle the words that describe the condition of being treated with <u>dignity</u>. Define *dignity*.

7. Underline the words that tell more about how the apprentices who had to be at <u>attention</u> needed to act. Who else might need to stand at *attention*?

8. Circle the words that compare something to the way one <u>snuffs</u> out a candle. Define *snuffs*.

Name _____ Date _____

from **A Christmas Carol: Scrooge and Marley,** *Act I, Scenes 2 & 5* by Israel Horovitz
Literary Analysis: Comparing Characters

A **character** is a person who takes part in a literary work. Like main characters in stories and novels, main characters in drama have traits that make them unique. These may include qualities such as dependability, intelligence, selfishness, and stubbornness. The characters in dramas have motives, or reasons, for behaving the way they do. For example, one character may be motivated by compassion, while another may be motivated by guilt.

When you read a drama, pay attention to what each character says and does, and note the reactions those words and actions spark in others. Notice what those words and actions reveal about the character's traits and motives.

In drama, one way to develop a character is through a **foil,** a character whose behavior and attitude contrast with those of the main character. With a foil, audiences can see good in contrast with bad or generousness in contrast with selfishness.

DIRECTIONS: *Answer the following questions to compare the older Scrooge with Fezziwig.*

Question	Scrooge	Fezziwig
1. What does the character say?		
2. What does the character do?		
3. How does the character react to Christmas?		
4. What do other characters say to or about him?		
5. What adjectives describe the character?		

Name _____ Date _____

from **A Christmas Carol: Scrooge and Marley,** *Act I, Scenes 2 & 5* by Israel Horovitz
Vocabulary Builder

Word List

fiddler	suitors	snuffs

A. DIRECTIONS: *Complete the word maps by writing a definition, synonyms, and an example sentence for each word from the Word List.*

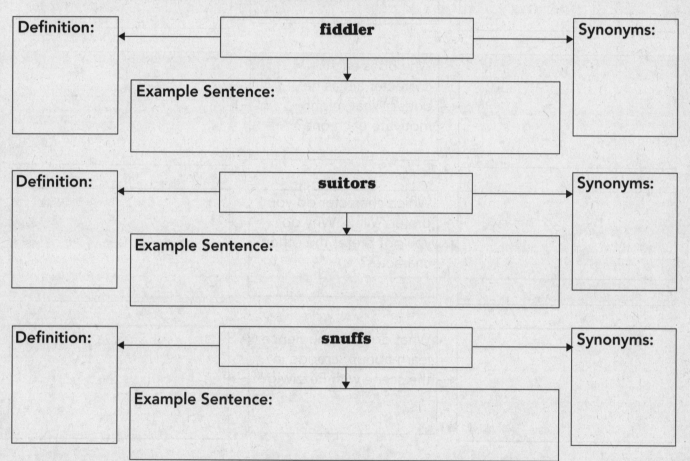

B. DIRECTIONS: *Write the letter of the word whose meaning is* most like *that of the word from the Word List.*

____ 1. fiddler
    A. crab   B. musician   C. violinist   D. tinkerer

____ 2. suitors
    A. boyfriends   B. tailors   C. lawyers   D. apprentices

____ 3. snuffs
    A. sniffs   B. erases   C. blots   D. extinguishes

Name _____ Date _____

Support for Writing to Compare Literary Works

Use this graphic organizer to gather notes for an essay in which you compare and contrast Fezziwig and Scrooge.

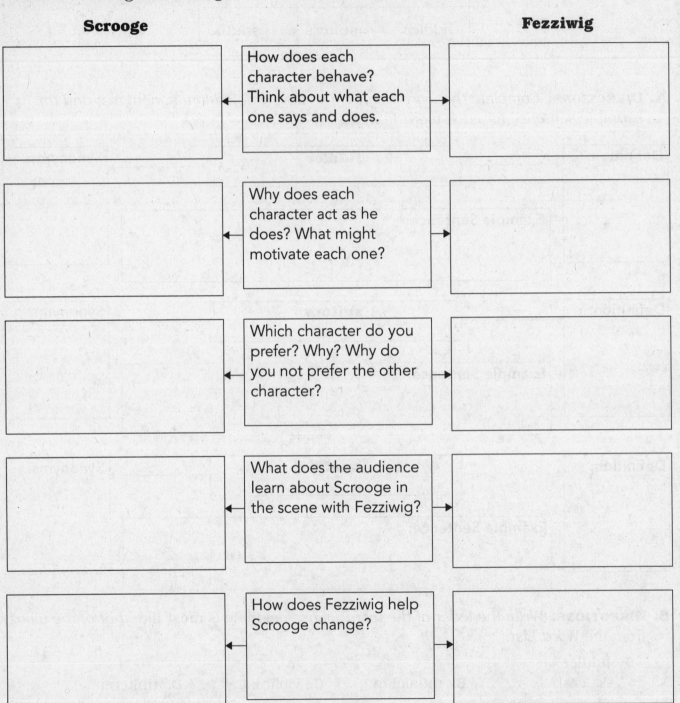

Scrooge   **Fezziwig**

How does each character behave? Think about what each one says and does.

Why does each character act as he does? What might motivate each one?

Which character do you prefer? Why? Why do you not prefer the other character?

What does the audience learn about Scrooge in the scene with Fezziwig?

How does Fezziwig help Scrooge change?

Now, use your notes to write an essay comparing and contrasting Fezziwig and Scrooge. Be sure to discuss how each character's actions and words help the playwright make a point about Scrooge and his behavior.

Name _____ Date _____

from A Christmas Carol: Scrooge and Marley, *Act I, Scenes 2 & 5* by Israel Horovitz
Selection Test A

Critical Reading *Identify the letter of the choice that best answers the question.*

____ 1. In Act I, Scene 2, of *A Christmas Carol: Scrooge and Marley,* why is Bob Cratchit eager to go home?

   A. It is cold in the office.

   B. It is Christmas Eve.

   C. He does not like Scrooge.

   D. He fears he will be asked to work late.

____ 2. According to Act I, Scene 2, of *A Christmas Carol: Scrooge and Marley,* why does Scrooge dislike the idea of giving Cratchit a day off?

   A. Scrooge must pay him for the day.

   B. Cratchit does not work very hard.

   C. It is expected to be a busy day.

   D. Scrooge does not like Christmas.

____ 3. According to Act I, Scene 2, of *A Christmas Carol: Scrooge and Marley,* what is it that Cratchit tries to say to Scrooge that Scrooge does not want to hear?

   A. "I would like tomorrow off."

   B. "Have a good evening."

   C. "Christmas comes only once a year."

   D. "Merry Christmas."

____ 4. In Act I, Scene 2, of *A Christmas Carol: Scrooge and Marley,* why does Cratchit rush away after he says, "Merry Christmas, Mr. Scrooge"?

   A. He fears that Scrooge will ask him to work late.

   B. He knows that he has made Scrooge angry.

   C. He knows that Scrooge does not celebrate Christmas.

   D. He knows that Scrooge is also in a hurry to leave.

____ 5. Which word gives the best overall description of Scrooge in Act I, Scene 2, of *A Christmas Carol: Scrooge and Marley*?

   A. insincere

   B. greedy

   C. kind

   D. loud

Name _____   Date _____

_____ 6. According to Act I, Scene 5, of *A Christmas Carol: Scrooge and Marley*, what is the relationship between Fezziwig and young Scrooge?
   A. Fezziwig is Scrooge's uncle.
   B. Fezziwig is Scrooge's teacher.
   C. Fezziwig is Scrooge's master.
   D. Fezziwig is Scrooge's father.

_____ 7. In Act I, Scene 5, of *A Christmas Carol: Scrooge and Marley*, why does Fezziwig tell Dick Wilkins and Scrooge to stop working?
   A. He cannot pay their salary.
   B. He is going to scold them.
   C. It is the end of the day.
   D. It is Christmas Eve.

_____ 8. In the Christmas festivities that take place in Act I, Scene 5, of *A Christmas Carol: Scrooge and Marley*, whom does Fezziwig include?
   A. just his family
   B. just his employees
   C. just his friends
   D. everyone

_____ 9. According to Act I, Scene 5, of *A Christmas Carol: Scrooge and Marley*, how do Dick Wilkins and the young Scrooge feel about Mr. Fezziwig?
   A. They do not think about him.
   B. They dislike him.
   C. They think he is fair, but dull.
   D. They admire him.

_____ 10. Which word gives the best overall description of Fezziwig in Act I, Scene 5, of *A Christmas Carol: Scrooge and Marley*?
   A. generous
   B. businesslike
   C. sincere
   D. silly

_____ 11. Fezziwig, in Act I, Scene 5, of *A Christmas Carol: Scrooge and Marley*, is contrasted with Scrooge in Scene 2. In drama, what is the name for a character who is contrasted with another character to help develop that character?
   A. a main character
   B. a motivated character
   C. a foil
   D. an understudy

____ **12.** Which statement does *not* accurately describe Fezziwig and Scrooge?

    A. Fezziwig is poor; Scrooge is wealthy.

    B. Fezziwig has family; Scrooge is alone.

    C. Fezziwig is kind; Scrooge is harsh.

    D. Fezziwig is giving; Scrooge is selfish.

Vocabulary

____ **13.** Which is an instrument that a *fiddler* would play?

    A. a harp

    B. a guitar

    C. a drum

    D. a violin

____ **14.** Why are *suitors* following Fezziwig's daughters?

    A. They are interested in marrying them.

    B. They are the daughters' servants.

    C. They think the daughters are pretty.

    D. They are the daughters' tailors.

____ **15.** Which sentence uses the word *snuffs* correctly?

    A. The clerk <u>snuffs</u> the documents before presenting them to his boss.

    B. On the coldest days, we wear earmuffs, <u>snuffs</u>, and lined gloves.

    C. The waitress <u>snuffs</u> the candles at each table at the end of her shift.

    D. The baker proudly placed one dozen frosted <u>snuffs</u> in the box.

Essay

16. Ebenezer Scrooge has his own business and employs one assistant. In an essay, describe Scrooge as a boss. How does he treat his employee? Is he fair? Is he understanding? Would you want to work for someone like him? Why or why not? Cite two details from Act I, Scene 2, of *A Christmas Carol: Scrooge and Marley* to support your response.

17. Like Scrooge, Fezziwig owns a business. He has two apprentices, and he has a family. In an essay, tell more about Fezziwig. What is he like? How does he treat his employees? Is he fair? Is he understanding? What do others think of him? Would you want to work for someone like him? Why or why not? Cite two details from Act I, Scene 5, of *A Christmas Carol: Scrooge and Marley* to support your response.

Name _____ Date _____

***from* A Christmas Carol: Scrooge and Marley,** *Act I, Scenes 2 & 5* by Israel Horovitz
Selection Test B

Critical Reading *Identify the letter of the choice that best completes the statement or answers the question.*

_____ 1. According to Act I, Scene 2, of *A Christmas Carol: Scrooge and Marley,* Scrooge resents having to give Bob Cratchit a day off for Christmas because
A. he knows that the firm will be busy on Christmas Day.
B. he dislikes being alone on Christmas Day.
C. he does not want to pay Cratchit for a day he does not work.
D. he had planned to fire Cratchit on Christmas Day.

_____ 2. In Act I, Scene 2, of *A Christmas Carol: Scrooge and Marley,* what does Scrooge suggest that Cratchit is doing by receiving a day's wages without working for it?
A. cheating him
B. mocking his business
C. picking his pocket
D. making excuses

_____ 3. According to Act I, Scene 2, of *A Christmas Carol: Scrooge and Marley,* why does Scrooge object when people enjoy Christmas?
A. He feels sad on Christmas because Marley died on Christmas Eve.
B. He cares only for making money, and Christmas interrupts business.
C. He believes that people should be kind and generous all year round.
D. He believes poor people should always be unhappy, even at Christmas.

_____ 4. In Act I, Scene 2, of *A Christmas Carol: Scrooge and Marley,* why does Cratchit wait until he is ready to leave to wish Scrooge a merry Christmas?
A. Cratchit knows that Scrooge will be insulted if he does not say it.
B. Cratchit is afraid that Scrooge will fire him for saying it.
C. Cratchit is afraid that Scrooge might throw something at him.
D. Cratchit knows that Scrooge does not want him to mention Christmas.

_____ 5. Which word best describes Scrooge's motivation in Act I, Scene 2, of *A Christmas Carol: Scrooge and Marley?*
A. hatred
B. pain
C. greed
D. happiness

_____ 6. According to Act I, Scene 5, of *A Christmas Carol: Scrooge and Marley,* what is the relationship between Scrooge and Fezziwig?
A. Scrooge is Fezziwig's servant.
B. Scrooge is Fezziwig's nephew.
C. Scrooge is Fezziwig's student.
D. Scrooge is Fezziwig's apprentice.

____ 7. According to Act I, Scene 5 of *A Christmas Carol: Scrooge and Marley*, what is the relationship between Scrooge and Dick Wilkins?
A. Wilkins is Scrooge's employer.
B. Scrooge is Wilkins's employer.
C. Scrooge and Wilkins are partners.
D. Wilkins and Scrooge are apprentices.

____ 8. According to Act I, Scene 5, of *A Christmas Carol: Scrooge and Marley*, who was kind to Scrooge in his past?
   I. Fezziwig
   II. the fiddler
   III. Fezziwig's daughters
   IV. Dick Wilkins
A. I, II, III
B. I, III, IV
C. I, II, IV
D. II, III, IV

____ 9. According to Act I, Scene 5, of *A Christmas Carol: Scrooge and Marley*, Fezziwig's Christmas festivities include
A. only Fezziwig's family.
B. only Fezziwig's employees.
C. only Fezziwig's daughters' suitors.
D. Fezziwig's family, his employees, and his daughters' suitors.

____ 10. According to Act I, Scene 5, of *A Christmas Carol: Scrooge and Marley*, what does young Scrooge feel toward Fezziwig?
A. gratitude
B. love
C. dignity
D. disrespect

____ 11. What is ironic about this statement by young Scrooge in Act I, Scene 5, of *A Christmas Carol: Scrooge and Marley*?

   If ever I own a firm of my own, I shall treat my apprentices with the same dignity and the same grace.

A. Although young Scrooge thinks his master is nice, the man treats others unkindly.
B. After young Scrooge says this, his master mistreats him and fires him.
C. Scrooge remains an apprentice all his life and is never again treated so well.
D. When Scrooge does have his own firm, he treats his employee harshly.

____ 12. Which adjectives best describe Fezziwig?
A. silly and happy
B. kind and intelligent
C. jolly and fat
D. kind and generous

____ 13. How does Fezziwig's treatment of others in Act I, Scene 5, of *A Christmas Carol: Scrooge and Marley* contrast with Scrooge's treatment of others in Scene 2?
   A. Fezziwig is generous to everyone while Scrooge is cold and harsh to everyone.
   B. Fezziwig is not serious about work while Scrooge is dedicated to his business.
   C. Fezziwig is foolish and silly while Scrooge is intelligent and serious.
   D. Fezziwig treats his wife and children well while Scrooge neglects his family.

____ 14. How does Fezziwig, in Act I, Scene 5, of *A Christmas Carol: Scrooge and Marley*, fulfill the role of a *foil*?
   A. He reinforces the theme of the play.
   B. He serves as a contrast to Scrooge.
   C. He adds comic relief to the play.
   D. He frustrates Scrooge's ambitions.

Vocabulary

____ 15. In Act I, Scene 5, of *A Christmas Carol: Scrooge and Marley*, whom can the reader assume the *suitors* have come to see?
   A. Fezziwig
   B. Fezziwig's daughters
   C. Fezziwig's wife
   D. Scrooge and Wilkins

____ 16. Before leaving for the evening, Cratchit *snuffs* out
   A. a document.
   B. a candle.
   C. the clock.
   D. the lights.

____ 17. In which sentence is the word *fiddler* used correctly?
   A. The *fiddler* in the country band played his violin energetically.
   B. The *fiddler* in the service station tuned up the engine perfectly.
   C. The *fiddler* in the orchestra tuned all of the stringed instruments.
   D. The *fiddler* in the accounting department audited the firm's records.

Essay

18. The brief dialogue between Scrooge and Cratchit in Act I, Scene 2, of *A Christmas Carol: Scrooge and Marley* gives the audience a great deal of insight into Scrooge's character. In an essay, compare Scrooge's character with Cratchit's. Answer these questions: What kind of man is Scrooge? How does he treat his employee? What kind of man is Bob Cratchit? How does he treat his employer? Which man would make a better boss? Why? In your response, cite at least two details from the excerpt of Scene 2.

19. Young Ebenezer Scrooge, in Act I, Scene 5, of *A Christmas Carol: Scrooge and Marley*, is very different from the Ebenezer Scrooge of Scene 2. In an essay, contrast the young Scrooge and the older Scrooge. What differences do you see in their actions? What differences do you see in what they say? What differences do you see in how they treat other people? Refer to at least one detail from each scene to support your points.

Name _____ Date _____

Writing Workshop—Unit 5, Part 1
Research: Multimedia Report

Prewriting: Gathering Details

Answer the questions in the chart below to help you choose your visual and audio sources.

Questions	Your Answers
What is your presentation about?	
Who is your audience?	
What is your purpose?	
What audio sources could you creatively use in your presentation?	
What video sources could you creatively use in your presentation?	

Drafting: Providing Elaboration

Use the following graphic organizer to help you decide how to use audio and visual aids to enhance your presentation.

Audio Aids	Visual Aids
What audio aids can you use?	What visual aids can you use?
When should you use audio aids?	When should you use visual aids?
How will the audio aid support your presentation?	How will the visual aid support your presentation?

Name _____ Date _____

Multimedia Report: Integrating Grammar Skills

Revising to Avoid Common Usage Problems

Be careful to use the following words correctly in your writing.

Word	Meaning	Example
Accept	*verb*, "to agree to" or "to take what is offered"	Everyone *except* Jo will *accept* what I have to say.
Except	*preposition*, "leaving out" or "other than"	
Affect	*verb*, "to influence" or "to cause a change in"	Too much sun can *affect* your eyes, although the *effect* is usually temporary.
Effect	usually a noun, means "a result"	
Advice	*noun*, "an opinion"	I listen to good *advice* and *advise* others as best I can.
Advise	*verb*, "to give an opinion"	
Beside	*preposition*, "at the side of" or "close to"	Did anyone *besides* Jon sit *beside* the waterfall?
Besides	*preposition*, "in addition to" or "other than"	
In	*preposition*, refers to position	I went *into* the car and then sat *in* traffic for hours.
Into	*preposition*, suggests motion	

Identifying Correct Usage

A. DIRECTIONS: *Complete each sentence by circling the correct choice in parentheses.*

1. I sat (beside, besides) Sandy at the basketball game after school.
2. Everyone (accept, except) Sharon went to the game.
3. Sharon went (in, into) the guidance counselor's office.
4. The counselor offered her good (advice, advise) about schoolwork.
5. Following the suggestions may have an (affect, effect) on Sharon's grades.

Fixing Common Usage Problems

B. DIRECTIONS: *On the lines provided, rewrite these sentences so that they use the correct words. If a sentence is correct as presented, write* correct.

1. Did anyone except Lola accept the invitation?

   _____

2. I would advice you to go in the house before it rains.

   _____

3. Many people besides me except my mother's advise.

   _____

Unit 5: Drama
Part 1 Benchmark Test 9

MULTIPLE CHOICE

Reading Skill: Purpose for Reading *Read the selection. Then, answer the questions that follow.*

Thinking Big: The Man Who Changed Our View of the Universe

At the age of 30, Edwin Hubble—the "Hubble" of the Hubble Space Telescope, which gives us views of distant galaxies—was intrigued by the stars and the possibility of worlds beyond our own. In 1919, Hubble left his successful law practice and returned to the study of astronomy. Just a few years later, Hubble made some of the most important discoveries of all time. He found that there were galaxies beyond the Milky Way and discovered that the universe is continually expanding. Although Hubble died more than fifty years ago, scientists today are still "expanding" on Hubble's momentous discoveries.

1. What does the title of the selection suggest?
   A. The selection is a work of fiction.
   B. The selection is about important discoveries.
   C. The selection was written by a student.
   D. The selection is from an Internet Web site.

2. Based on the title and first sentence, which of the following best states a purpose for reading the selection?
   A. to learn about an important scientist
   B. to learn about the practice of law
   C. to be entertained by an amusing story
   D. to analyze a theory about the universe

3. Why is it important to preview the selection after setting a purpose for reading?
   A. to help you outline the main ideas and details
   B. to help you set more than one purpose for reading
   C. to help you identify unfamiliar words in the text
   D. to help you decide if the selection will fit your purpose

4. Which of the following might best help you preview a literary work before reading it?
   A. the order in which events occur
   B. the author's biography
   C. the point of view of the narrator
   D. the way the text is organized

Read the selection. Then, answer the questions that follow.

Using the Memory Function of Your Cell Phone

Let's face it: you're on the go. And you've got a lot on your mind. You can't be expected to remember all the important phone numbers you need to know. Let your phone remember them for you. Here's how to use the phone memory feature:

1. Enter the phone number you want to store.
2. Press *STO* to begin storing. You will see: *Location XX?*
3. Press *STO* again to store the sequence in the displayed location.
4. Enter a digit and press the star key to store the sequence in the first available location beginning with that digit.
5. Scroll through the icons and press *STO* to select a highlighted icon.

5. Why might you read the introduction more quickly than the directions in this selection?
   - A. The introduction is more important to understanding the task.
   - B. The introduction is written at a simpler level.
   - C. The introduction is more promotional than useful.
   - D. The introduction is written as a paragraph.

6. Which of the following is best read slowly?
   - A. a recipe with many steps
   - B. an advertisement for toothpaste
   - C. a comic strip
   - D. an exciting short story

7. Which of the following influences your reading rate?
   - A. the author's purpose
   - B. your purpose for reading
   - C. the length of the text
   - D. the author's skill as a writer

Read the selection. Then, answer the questions that follow.

Think you've read *Charlotte's Web*? Read it again. You'll find this American classic to be full of surprises you missed during first reading. As almost everyone knows, the book by E. B. White, is the story of a girl who befriends a runt of a pig named Wilbur. The girl saves Wilbur's life, which is again saved, later in the story, by a remarkable spider named Charlotte. *Charlotte's Web* is an elegantly written fantasy with moral overtones and gentle wisdom about life and death.

8. What is one purpose for reading literary criticism such as the selection?
   - A. to decide whether to read a work
   - B. to analyze a literary work
   - C. to learn about a book's author
   - D. to judge a literary work

9. Which phrase from the selection best illustrates the critic's opinion of *Charlotte's Web*?
   - A. elegantly written fantasy
   - B. American classic
   - C. remarkable spider
   - D. gentle wisdom

10. Which of the following best describes the critic's feelings about *Charlotte's Web*?
   A. The critic thinks the book is charming.
   B. The critic admires E. B. White.
   C. The critic recommends the book.
   D. The critic strongly likes the book.

Literary Analysis: Dialogue *Read the selection. Then, answer the questions that follow.*

Brendan joined his brother outside the school. "I lost the election," he told Sam.

"What?!" Sam exclaimed, and then narrowed his eyes. "You are the world's *greatest* pessimist," he said. "Have they counted all the votes?"

Brendan shrugged and glanced woefully to the side, "Well—no. But I just came from the gym and I could just *feel* that the votes weren't going my way."

"Come on, buddy," Sam said, heading back into the school. "We're going to stay until we know for sure whether or not you won. I don't want to spend an evening with you moaning about losing—especially if you won."

11. Which of the following best describes dialogue in a literary work?
   A. a conversation between characters
   B. a portrait of a character
   C. a way a writer reveals the plot
   D. a struggle between opposing forces

12. What does the dialogue in the selection reveal about Sam?
   A. He is older than Brendan.
   B. He is supportive of Brendan.
   C. He often disagrees with Brendan.
   D. He is jealous of Brendan.

13. Why is the last line "Come on, buddy" significant?
   A. It shows that Sam is impatient.
   B. It shows that Sam is playful.
   C. It shows Sam's affection for Brendan.
   D. It shows Sam's teasing nature.

Literary Analysis: Stage Directions *Read the stage directions below. Then, answer the questions that follow.*

[It is early morning in the Vargas house. Kyle's parents and his sister are still asleep. The faint light of dawn can be seen through the window of Kyle's bedroom, where he stands in front of a full-length mirror. In the distance can be heard the sound of a chirping bird. Kyle holds several note cards in his hand. He studies one of the cards for a minute. Then he squares his shoulders, looks confidently into the mirror, and recites the opening line of his speech.]

14. What are stage directions in a dramatic script?
   A. the way in which events unfold
   B. the words not spoken by characters
   C. the central message in a play
   D. conversations among characters

15. What information about the setting is included in the stage directions of the selection?
    A. the type of speech Kyle will give
    B. the first line of Kyle's speech
    C. a description of the lighting
    D. the theme of the play

16. To whom might these stage directions be most useful?
    A. to someone who is reading the play
    B. to someone who is reviewing the play
    C. to someone who is watching the play
    D. to the author of the play

Literary Analysis: Comparing Characters *Read the excerpt from a dramatic script. Then, answer the questions that follow.*

ANNE. [*She studies a receipt.*] The clerk forgot to charge me for one of these books.

JOANIE. Great! You got a free book, then.

ANNE. What? Are you saying that I shouldn't go back and tell him?

JOANIE. Don't be silly. The store probably won't notice, so just consider it a little gift. Besides, that store charges too much for books.

ANNE. I'd feel terrible. I couldn't enjoy the book for thinking about not paying for it. It's just not right.

JOANIE. [*Shaking her head.*] Suit yourself. But I think you're being too righteous about the whole thing.

17. Which of the following best describes Anne?
    A. careful
    B. confused
    C. silly
    D. honest

18. Based on the selection, Which of the following is probably true of Joanie?
    A. She is uncomfortable around Anne.
    B. She has a strong sense of fairness.
    C. She can justify being dishonest.
    D. She is easily influenced by Anne.

19. How are Anne and Joanie different?
    A. Anne is more concerned than Joanie about what others think.
    B. Anne is more influenced by her conscience than is Joanie.
    C. Joanie thinks things through more carefully than does Anne.
    D. Joanie is more easily upset than is Anne.

Vocabulary: Suffixes

20. What is the meaning of *attachment* in the following sentence?

The stray puppy formed a strong attachment to Gil's dog.

    A. the act of fastening
    B. the quality of being connected
    C. capable of holding
    D. one who attaches

21. Which of the following is the best definition of *discouragement* in the following sentence?

With no trace of discouragement, Ari began the task for the third time.

    A. the act of being hopeful   C. the condition of being less determined

    B. having or showing courage   D. capable of losing hope

22. What does the word *construction* mean in the following sentence?

The cost of the construction of a new gym was less than expected.

    A. the act of building   C. a completed structure

    B. to cause to be made   D. one skilled in building

23. Which of the following is the best definition of *amusement* in the following sentence?

Minh chuckled with amusement at the street performer's pantomime.

    A. tending to cause laughter   C. the act of pleasing someone

    B. full of delight   D. the condition of being entertained

24. What is the meaning of *donation* in the following sentence?

Ms. Wiley made a generous donation to the hurricane-relief fund.

    A. to cause to be given   C. someone who makes a gift

    B. the process of giving   D. something that is given

25. What is the best definition of *rotation* in the following sentence?

The flashing rotation of the wooden top enchanted the small child.

    A. the state of changing   C. capable of spinning

    B. the act of turning   D. something that revolves

Grammar: Using Interjections

26. Which of the following best describes an interjection?

    A. a word used to join groups of words   C. a part of speech that expresses emotion

    B. a noun that identifies another noun   D. a part of speech that modifies a verb

27. Which of the following sentences contains an interjection?

    A. Where did you put the box of clothes?   C. All of the coins are missing!

    B. The actor groaned miserably.   D. Oops, I think I pressed the wrong key.

28. Which word in the following sentence is an interjection?

Wow, aren't computers amazing?

    A. Wow   C. computers

    B. aren't   D. amazing

Grammar: Double Negatives

29. Which of the following words is a negative word?

Alejandro remarked bitterly that they were going nowhere slowly.

A. remarked   C. nowhere
B. bitterly   D. slowly

30. What is the best way to correct the double negative in the following sentence?

I never see no one I know at the park.

A. I never see anyone I know at the park.   C. I never do not see anyone I know at the park.
B. I do not ever see nobody I know at the park.   D. I do not see no one I know at the park.

31. Which of the following sentences contains a double negative?
A. Tanya will not go near the ocean.   C. I never listen to anyone who gossips.
B. Mr. Fell had nothing bad to say.   D. We do not have no extra tables.

Grammar: Revising to Avoid Common Usage Problems

32. What is the meaning of *affect* in the following sentence?

The wet weather did not affect Josh's performance in the bike race.

A. bring about   C. result in
B. influence   D. cause

33. In which sentence is *accept* used correctly?
A. Trenell made all A's accept in science.   C. I like all vegetables accept beets.
B. Everyone accept Bonnie was there.   D. Will the writer accept both awards?

ESSAY

Writing

34. Suppose that your school is considering adding tap dancing as a PE course. Write a brief letter to your principal giving your opinion about the decision. State at least two reasons and provide supporting details. Remember to include a salutation and your signature in your letter. Remember to state a firm point of view.

35. Think of a friend, family member, or neighbor who has qualities that you admire. Write a brief tribute, or expression of admiration, to this person. Your tribute can include a story of a time when this person particularly influenced you, or write about two or three qualities that you most admire in this person. Write a concluding statement at the end of your tribute.

36. Write a paragraph that describes a plan for a multimedia report. In your plan, tell about the topic of the report and describe how the report will be organized. Describe the media—print and nonprint—that you plan to use and tell about the effect you hope to create in the report.

Unit 5: Drama
Part 2 Concept Map

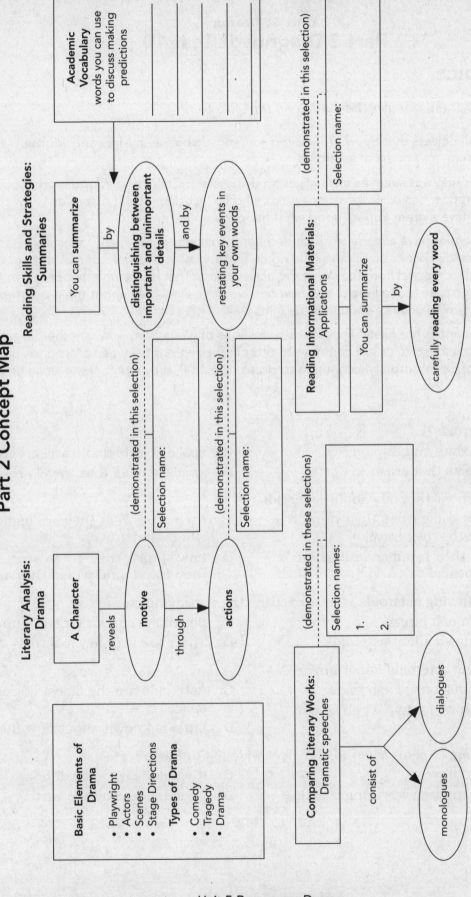

Reading Skills and Strategies:
Summaries

You can summarize

by

distinguishing between important and unimportant details

and by

restating key events in your own words

Academic Vocabulary words you can use to discuss making predictions

(demonstrated in this selection)

Selection name:

(demonstrated in this selection)

Selection name:

Reading Informational Materials:
Applications

You can summarize

by

carefully reading every word

Literary Analysis:
Drama

A Character

reveals

motive

through

actions

Basic Elements of Drama

- Playwright
- Actors
- Scenes
- Stage Directions

Types of Drama

- Comedy
- Tragedy
- Drama

Comparing Literary Works:
Dramatic speeches

consist of

dialogues

monologues

(demonstrated in these selections)

Selection names:

1.
2.

Part 2 Student Log

Complete this chart to track your assignments.

Writing	Writing Workshop	Other Assignments

Extend Your Learning	

Name _____ Date _____

MULTIPLE CHOICE

Read the selection. Then, answer the questions that follow.

Asteroids are small objects that travel around the sun, mostly between Mars and Jupiter. Astronomers study the size, structure, and paths of asteroids.

Studying asteroids may not seem as exciting as studying stars. Collecting information about star systems is on a much grander scale. However, scientists who collect data about asteroids know that their work may someday have a great impact upon what happens on Earth.

In fact, several asteroids have already crash-landed here. That was many, many years ago. Bits of space rock so small that they go unseen are always landing on Earth. However chunks of rock sixty or eighty feet wide have occasionally dropped from the sky in the ancient past. That is just what happened in Arizona thousands of years ago. Like that asteroid, any new one would leave a hole about three-quarters of a mile wide and vaporize anything unlucky enough to be in its way.

However, that scenario is not likely. Thousands or millions of years from now, another large asteroid might fall. For now, most asteroids will continue to orbit in the regions between Mars and Jupiter. Those that cross the path of Earth's orbit will continue to do so, too. Still, they won't come close enough to scare us.

1. What are asteroids?
   A. moons of Mars and Jupiter
   B. space objects that crash to Earth
   C. space objects that travel around the sun
   D. space objects that travel around Earth

2. What do astronomers study about asteroids?
   A. where they came from, their number, and the paths they travel
   B. their size, their number, and where they are located
   C. their size, what they are made of, and where they travel
   D. how similar they are to stars, where they travel, and where they are located

3. Why might studying asteroids be less exciting than studying stars?
   A. Stars are much larger.
   B. Little is known about asteroids.
   C. Scientists can study stars up close.
   D. There are very few asteroids.

4. Why is studying asteroids important?
   A. There are millions of asteroids.
   B. Asteroids have an impact on Earth.
   C. Asteroids are the oldest objects in space.
   D. Little is known about how they travel.

5. What might happen if an asteroid sixty feet wide fell to Earth?
   A. It would go unseen.
   B. It would vaporize everything near it.
   C. It would leave a small hole.
   D. It would destroy the earth.

6. When did a large asteroid last strike Earth?
   A. Large asteroids have never landed on Earth.
   B. A large asteroid struck Earth thousands of years ago.
   C. A large asteroid struck Earth in the past century.
   D. Large asteroids land on Earth nearly every day.

7. How likely is it that a large asteroid might fall to Earth soon?
   A. Large asteroids never strike Earth.
   B. One could fall any time.
   C. It may be thousands of years.
   D. They strike Earth nearly every day.

Read the selection. Then, answer the questions that follow.

Many scientists are working in a new field called biometrics to reliably identify individuals. A person's signature is no longer a sure proof of identity. Too many people are able to copy the handwriting of others.

Biometrics looks at the physical things that are unique to each person. These include your fingerprints, the pattern in the colored part of your eyes, and the structure of your face and palms. Taking fingerprints and then scanning a person's fingers to check for a match is one new way to identify people. Researchers have created "the ID mouse." It looks like a computer mouse but scans a person's fingerprints.

Other researchers focus on photography that computers will recognize. For example, a scan of a person's face, eye, or palm must match what is in a computer to prove identity. Many people fear the consequences of too much personal information being collected. For example, a new card being tested includes fingerprints, eye scans, palm geometry, and a digital photo. However, if someone steals and uses this information, the theft of a person's identity would be complete.

Scientists can split an atom, but biometrics might be some of the trickiest research ever. How can you check and protect a person's identity at the same time?

8. What is biometrics?
   A. the study of people's signatures
   B. the study of handwriting
   C. a way of identifying individuals
   D. the study of the physical body

9. Why is handwriting not a good way to identify someone?
   A. It's hard to get a person's handwriting.
   B. Everyone's handwriting is different.
   C. Handwriting is hard to analyze.
   D. People can copy others' handwriting.

10. Which of the following are unique physical things studied in biometrics?
    A. handwriting and fingerprints
    B. hair color and shoe size
    C. eye color and signature
    D. fingerprints and structure of face

11. What special thing is used to scan fingerprints?
    A. a computer
    B. an ID mouse
    C. a camera
    D. a computer mouse

12. What photographic information about a person might a computer store for identification?
    A. a photograph of a person's signature
    B. a photograph of a person's face
    C. a collection of family photographs
    D. a digital photo of a person's heart

13. What new type of identification card is being tested?
   A. one with a person's fingerprints, eye scans, and photograph
   B. one with a digital recording of a person's voice
   C. one with a person's photograph and fingerprints
   D. one with a person's handwriting, eye scans, and photograph

14. Why is storing too much information about a person dangerous?
   A. A person's identity can easily be stolen.
   B. People's personal information changes.
   C. It is easier to have incorrect information.
   D. People will refuse to give information.

15. What is the challenge to biometrics researchers?
   A. to collect enough information about individuals to identify them
   B. to prevent individuals from stealing other people's identity
   C. to identify people and at the same time keep their identity safe from theft
   D. to develop computers and cameras that can accurately identify people

"The Monsters Are Due on Maple Street" by Rod Serling
Vocabulary Warm-up Word Lists

Study these words from "The Monsters Are Due on Maple Street." Then, complete the activities that follow.

Word List A

afford [uh FAWRD] *v.* to have enough money to buy something
   Susan made enough money to afford a new car.

broadcast [BRAWD kast] *n.* television or radio program
   I was in school when the first news broadcast about the attack on the Pentagon aired.

gradually [GRAJ oo uhl lee] *adv.* slowly but steadily
   To make a good soufflé, combine the ingredients gradually.

hesitant [HEZ i tuhnt] *adj.* unwilling to do something because you are unsure or worried
   Pat was hesitant to ask her parents for a new cell phone.

mildly [MYLD lee] *adv.* slightly
   We were only mildly interested in the senator's speech.

obviously [AHB vee uhs lee] *adv.* easily seen or understood
   The photographer was obviously more interested in nature than in cityscapes.

process [PROS es] *n.* series of actions or changes to achieve a particular result
   Jerry is in the process of rebuilding his glider.

typical [TIP i kuhl] *adj.* having the qualities of a particular thing, person, or group
   At age 2, the typical child talks in two-word sentences.

Word List B

dimension [di MEN shuhn] *n.* level of consciousness, existence, or reality
   We can go beyond ordinary time and space through the dimension of our imaginations.

intense [in TENS] *adj.* serious and having very strong feelings
   The president gave an intense speech on the problem of world hunger.

prejudices [prej uh dis ez] *n.* opinions formed hastily without careful thought
   People's prejudices are often based on fear or misinformation.

reaction [ree AK shuhn] *n.* action or feeling in response to something
   The public reaction to the mayor's decision to resign was complete surprise.

reflective [ri FLEK tiv] *adj.* serious and thoughtful
   After watching the movie, James left the theater in a reflective mood.

residential [rez i DEN shuhl] *adj.* having to do with private homes
   We moved from the city to a quiet residential neighborhood.

tremendous [tri MEN duhs] *adj.* huge; enormous
   The audience gave the orchestra a tremendous ovation.

unique [yoo NEEK] *adj.* one of a kind; unlike anything else
   Because every set of fingerprints is unique, it is often used as a means of identification.

Name _____ Date _____

"The Monsters Are Due on Maple Street" by Rod Serling
Vocabulary Warm-up Exercises

Exercise A *Fill in each blank in the paragraph below with an appropriate word from Word List A. Use each word only once.*

Marcie couldn't [1] _____ to buy one of those hand-held music players,

so she listened to a music [2] _____ on her portable radio. At first she

was [3] _____ to admit to her friends that she listened to the radio, but

one day that changed. While Marcie was in the [4] _____ of adjusting

the radio tuner, she came across a public radio station. She listened for a while and

discovered that the programs were not [5] _____ of other stations.

[6] _____, she tuned into this station more and more. She enjoyed the

lively conversations about world events. When she told her friends, they were only

[7] _____ interested. [8] _____, her friends wanted to

listen only to music. Marcie felt they were missing something special.

Exercise B *Circle* T *if the statement is true or* F *if the statement is false. Then, explain your answer.*

1. Reaching the top of Mount Everest is a <u>tremendous</u> accomplishment.
   T / F _____

2. A <u>residential</u> area is a great place to go camping.
   T / F _____

3. If you lose something <u>unique</u> you can always get another one.
   T / F _____

4. It is always fun to be with a person who is very <u>intense</u>.
   T / F _____

5. It is natural to be <u>reflective</u> when you are in a hurry.
   T / F _____

6. Dreams occur in another <u>dimension</u>.
   T / F _____

7. One typical audience <u>reaction</u> to a good horror movie is lots of screaming.
   T / F _____

8. A person can never overcome his or her <u>prejudices</u>.
   T / F _____

Name _____ Date _____

"The Monsters Are Due on Maple Street" by Rod Serling
Reading Warm-up A

Read the following passage. Pay special attention to the underlined words. Then, read it again, and complete the activities. Use a separate sheet of paper for your written answers.

If you had a time machine in your home, would you use it? Chances are you would. Maybe you already do, for there really is a time machine in your home. It's tucked inside your TV. Today you can turn on the cable channels that rerun old television shows and witness life in America as far back as 1950.

Before 1950, home televisions had been around for about three years, but most people couldn't <u>afford</u> them. The <u>typical</u> set was a big wooden box with a tiny 10-inch or 15-inch video screen. The picture was black and white and fuzzy. TVs were expensive because they were new and excitingly different. Unfortunately, the shows were only <u>mildly</u> entertaining. One popular show was wrestling. The viewers were wild about a wrestler named Gorgeous George. He wore hairpins in his hair.

<u>Gradually</u>, the screens got bigger. The picture improved, and so did the shows. By the early 1950s, stations offered several kinds of programs: plays, newscasts, old movies, variety and talent shows. A favorite <u>broadcast</u> of the '50s was the situation comedy, or "sitcom." Sitcoms, such as *I Love Lucy*, found the humor in everyday life.

Commercials were really big, too, even then. By 1954, television manufacturers were in the <u>process</u> of discontinuing black-and-white TVs and introducing color. People were no longer <u>hesitant</u> to buy a TV set. Everybody was eager to have one.

It was during the '50s that families started eating prepackaged dinners while watching their favorite TV shows. Americans also began to believe that the families shown on *Leave It to Beaver* and *Father Knows Best* represented the normal American family—so what was wrong with *their* families? <u>Obviously</u>, early TV often presented an unreal picture of real America. Still, much that was on TV then was just as real as it is today. Keep that in mind the next time you watch a rerun, grab a TV dinner, and travel back to the '50s.

1. Circle the word that tells what people couldn't <u>afford</u>. Write the meaning of *afford*.

2. Underline the words that describe a <u>typical</u> TV set of the '50s. Describe a *typical* TV set of today.

3. Circle the word described as only <u>mildly</u> entertaining. Rewrite the sentence using a synonym for *mildly*.

4. Underline the words that tell what happened <u>gradually</u>. Write about something else that happens *gradually*.

5. Underline the words that name a favorite <u>broadcast</u> of the '50s. Write about your favorite kind of *broadcast*.

6. Underline the words that tell what manufacturers were in the <u>process</u> of doing by 1954. Write about something you are in the *process* of doing.

7. Circle the word that means the opposite of <u>hesitant</u>. Write the meaning of *hesitant*.

8. Underline the words that tell what early TV <u>obviously</u> presented. Use a synonym for *obviously* in a sentence about TV.

"The Monsters Are Due on Maple Street" by Rod Serling
Reading Warm-up B

Read the following passage. Pay special attention to the underlined words. Then, read it again, and complete the activities. Use a separate sheet of paper for your written answers.

On October 2, 1959, the first episode of a science-fiction/fantasy show appeared on television. It was a "little show," only 30 minutes long, and in black and white, but it lit up the TV screen like nothing before. Perhaps you have heard of it. It was called *The Twilight Zone.*

In all of television, *The Twilight Zone* was <u>unique</u>; there was no other show like it at the time. Viewers didn't just watch it—they entered it. Each week they would find themselves in another small town, on a <u>residential</u> street lined with modest houses, or in a building that looked familiar, but not quite. They entered a <u>dimension</u> between dreams and imagination, but it felt like home. They left it feeling thoughtful and <u>reflective</u>.

Before each episode, Rod Serling, the writer and creator of the series, delivered a short but <u>intense</u> introduction.

NARRATOR'S VOICE. *Maple Street. Six-forty-four p.m. on a late September evening. [A pause] Maple Street in the last calm and reflective moment . . . before the monsters came!*

Although it was considered science fiction, *The Twilight Zone* was unlike later sci-fi shows that were set in another time and place. Many of the stories did take place in a not-too-distant future, and alien monsters occasionally would make an appearance. However, it was the monster within the human heart that most interested Rod Serling. His scripts explored political and social issues, <u>prejudices</u> against ideas and other people, injustice, and other human failings. His shows were a <u>tremendous</u> departure from other TV shows of the time, which were usually predictable and never political. Viewer <u>reaction</u> to *The Twilight Zone* proved that audiences were ready for more thoughtful programs.

The show still has loyal fans, not only because the stories are timeless, but also because, as Rod Serling would be the first to tell you, "At one time or another, we all live in *The Twilight Zone.*"

1. Underline the words that give the meaning of <u>unique</u>. Write a sentence using the word *unique*.

2. Underline the words that describe a <u>residential</u> street. Describe a *residential* street in your area.

3. Underline the words that describe the <u>dimension</u> viewers entered. Rewrite the sentence using a synonym for *dimension*.

4. Circle the word that means the same as <u>reflective</u>. Write a sentence using the word *reflective*.

5. Circle the word that tells what was short but <u>intense</u>. Describe a person you know or have read about who is *intense*.

6. Underline the words that tell what <u>prejudices</u> are against. Use *prejudices* in a sentence.

7. Circle the words that tell what was a <u>tremendous</u> departure. Underline the words that tell what they were a *tremendous* departure from. Give a synonym for *tremendous*.

8. Underline the words that tell what viewer <u>reaction</u> proved. Write the meaning of *reaction*.

"The Monsters Are Due on Maple Street" by Rod Serling

Reading: Distinguish Between Important and Unimportant Details to Write a Summary

A **summary** is a brief statement that presents only the main ideas and most important details. Summarizing helps you review and understand what you are reading. To summarize, you must first **distinguish between important and unimportant details.** Ask yourself questions like these:

• Is the detail necessary to an understanding of the literary work?
• Would the work hold together without the inclusion of this information?

As you read, pause periodically to recall and restate only the key events and important details.

DIRECTIONS: *Read these summaries of portions of "The Monsters Are Due on Maple Street." Then, answer the questions that follow each summary.*

It is an ordinary September evening on Maple Street when a roar is heard and a flash is seen. The power goes off, and telephones and portable radios stop working. One neighbor leaves to see what is happening on another street. Another neighbor says that he will go downtown to find out what is going on. For no explainable reason, his car will not start. He and a third neighbor decide to walk downtown. Tommy, a fourteen-year-old boy who wears eyeglasses, tells the men not to go. Tommy tells the crowd that what is happening is like every story about aliens he has read. He says that before they land, aliens send a family that looks human to live in a community and prepare for the aliens' arrival.

1. What is the main idea of the preceding summary?

_____

_____

2. Which detail in the preceding summary is unnecessary?

_____

_____

After Les Goodman's car starts on its own, the neighbors become suspicious of Goodman. A neighbor says that she has seen him standing on his porch in the middle of the night, looking at the sky. Goodman explains that he often has insomnia. He compares his neighbors to frightened rabbits. He says that they are letting a nightmare begin.

3. What is the main idea of the preceding summary?

_____

_____

4. Which detail in the preceding summary is unimportant? How do you know it is unimportant?

_____

_____

Name _____   Date _____

"The Monsters Are Due on Maple Street" by Rod Serling
Literary Analysis: A Character's Motives

A character's motives are the reasons for his or her actions. Motives are usually related to what a character wants, needs, or feels. Powerful motives include love, anger, fear, and greed. As you read, think about what motivates each character.

DIRECTIONS: *Read the following passages from "The Monsters Are Due on Maple Street." Then, answer the questions that follow, about the characters' motives.*

> **STEVE.** It isn't just the power failure, Charlie. If it was, we'd still be able to get a broadcast on the portable.
>
> [*There's a murmur of reaction to this.* STEVE *looks from face to face and then over to his car.*]
>
> **STEVE.** I'll run downtown. We'll get this all straightened out.

1. What are Steve's motives for volunteering to go downtown?

   _____

   _____

> **GOODMAN.** I just don't understand it. I tried to start it and it wouldn't start. You saw me. All of you saw me.
>
> [*And now, just as suddenly as the engine started, it stops and there's a long silence that is gradually intruded upon by the frightened murmuring of the people.*]
>
> **GOODMAN.** I don't understand. I swear . . . I don't understand. What's happening?
>
> **DON.** Maybe you better tell us. Nothing's working on this street. Nothing. No lights, no power, no radio. . . . Nothing except one car—yours!
>
> [*The people pick this up and now their murmuring becomes a loud chant filling the air with accusations and demands for action. Two of the men . . . head toward* GOODMAN, *who backs away, backing into his car and now at bay.*]
>
> **GOODMAN.** Wait a minute now. You keep your distance—all of you. So I've got a car that starts by itself—well, that's a freak thing. I admit it. But does that make me some kind of a criminal or something? I don't know why the car works—it just does!

2. Which speaker appears to be motivated by confusion? _____

3. Which speaker appears to be motivated by suspicion? _____

4. What emotion or emotions appear to be motivating Goodman after the crowd has accused him? _____

5. Why might Goodman be feeling this emotion? _____

   _____

Name _____ Date _____

"The Monsters Are Due on Maple Street" by Rod Serling
Vocabulary Builder

Word List

flustered	sluggishly	persistently	defiant	metamorphosis

A. DIRECTIONS: *Read each sentence, and think about the meaning of the italicized word from the Word List. Then, answer the question, and explain your answer.*

1. Would you expect a *flustered* person to speak clearly?

   _____

2. If a heavy rain fills a riverbed, will the river move *sluggishly*?

   _____

3. If someone *persistently* asks a question, would you assume that she is eager to know the answer?

   _____

4. Would a *defiant* child be likely to refuse to do his chores?

   _____

5. If a rude person undergoes a *metamorphosis*, is she likely to continue to be rude?

   _____

B. DIRECTIONS: *Write the letter of the word or group of words whose meaning is* most nearly the opposite *of the word from the Word List.*

____ 1. flustered
   A. nervous   B. calm   C. neat   D. suspicious
____ 2. sluggishly
   A. speedily   B. hopefully   C. listlessly   D. carelessly
____ 3. persistently
   A. confidently   B. appreciatively C. halfheartedly D. importantly
____ 4. defiant
   A. responsive   B. weak   C. worthless   D. combative
____ 5. metamorphosis
   A. long speech   B. resistance   C. dejection   D. lack of change

"The Monsters Are Due on Maple Street" by Rod Serling
Support for Writing a Report

Use this chart to take notes for your **report** from the point of view of Figure One or Figure Two. In your report, you will inform your leader of the events on Maple Street.

Report to Leader on Visit to Maple Street, Earth

Human Beings

Steve: _____

_____

Tommy: _____

_____

Charlie: _____

_____

Pete Van Horn: _____

_____

Les Goodman: _____

_____

Other residents of Maple Street: _____

_____

_____

Events

Act I: _____

_____

_____

Act II: _____

_____

_____

Recommendations

_____

_____

_____

Now, write a draft of your report. Be sure to focus on the important details.

Name _____   Date _____

"The Monsters Are Due on Maple Street" by Rod Serling
Support for Extend Your Learning

Listening and Speaking

Use this worksheet as you discuss with a group of classmates your plans for staging a **scene** from "The Monsters Are Due on Maple Street."

Scene to be staged: _____

Group member acting as director: _____

Characters and group members playing the parts: _____

_____

_____

_____

Notes on performing my part: _____

_____

_____

_____

Research and Technology

Use this worksheet as you plan how you would **film the scene** you just presented.

Events that take place in the scene: _____

_____

_____

_____

Camera angles that best capture each event: _____

_____

_____

_____

When and how special effects should be used: _____

_____

_____

_____

Name _____ Date _____

"The Monsters Are Due on Maple Street" by Rod Serling
Enrichment: Script Writing

If any character in "The Monsters Are Due on Maple Street" reflects Rod Serling's philosophy, it is Steve Brand. Throughout the play, Steve tries to persuade his neighbors to choose reason and common sense over suspicion and violence.

DIRECTIONS: *Prepare to write a script for a half-hour science-fiction television series—a modern-day* Twilight Zone. *Like Serling, you will require ordinary people to face an extraordinary situation. And like Serling's work, your screenplay will teach a lesson as well as entertain. Gather your ideas by responding to the following prompts. (Read all the prompts before you begin writing. You may not want to respond in order.)*

Setting: When and where will the events take place? Will your screenplay be set in the present, in the past, or in the future? Will it take place on this planet, on another planet, or in a spacecraft? _____

_____

Characters: Will your characters be humans or aliens, or will the two interact? Think about your characters' beliefs, their education and family background, their occupation (are they adults who hold jobs? are they students?), their talents, their fears, their quirks. Describe two or three main characters, including the most important details.

_____

Plot: Here is where you have to figure out—and describe—what happens to your characters. The events should be very unusual, and they should create a problem for the characters to resolve. Briefly describe the plot, including the conflict and the resolution.

_____

_____

_____

Message: What lesson will your screenplay teach? Which character will convey the message? At what point will he or she do it?

_____

_____

Now, write the dialogue for one brief scene in your screenplay.

_____

_____

_____

_____

_____

_____

Name _____ Date _____

"The Monsters Are Due on Maple Street" by Rod Serling
Build Language Skills: Vocabulary

Suffixes: *-ize*

The suffix *-ize* (or *-yze*) means "to make." This suffix forms verbs. When you add *-ize* to the noun *summary*, for example, you create the verb *summarize*, meaning "to make a summary." When you add *-yze* to the noun *analysis*, you create the verb *analyze*, meaning "to make an analysis."

A. DIRECTIONS: *Add the suffix -ize or -yze to the italicized noun in each sentence. Then, write a sentence using the new verb.*

1. Put these names in order according to the letters of the *alphabet*.

    _____

2. Jason worked hard to make his dreams become *real*.

    _____

3. The scientists will work on an *analysis* of the evidence.

    _____

4. Can you commit this poem to *memory*?

    _____

5. The prairie dogs will form a *colony* on the plains.

    _____

Academic Vocabulary Practice

B. DIRECTIONS: *Revise each sentence so that the italicized Academic Vocabulary word is defined correctly or used logically. Be sure to use the vocabulary word in your revision.*

1. If you are arranging events in *chronological* order, you may arrange them in any order.

    _____

2. When asked to describe the *sequence* of events, the witness began with the end of the story, skipped to the middle, and ended with the beginning.

    _____

3. When you *summarize* a work, you tell everything that happened in the order in which it happened.

    _____

4. A *characteristic* is a quality that makes one thing just like another thing.

    _____

5. To *focus* on a scene is to look at it as if from a distance, so that it is blurry and indistinct.

    _____

Name _____ Date _____

"The Monsters Are Due on Maple Street" by Rod Serling
Build Language Skills: Grammar

Sentence Functions and Endmarks

Sentences are classified into four categories, according to their function.

Category, Function, and Endmark	Example
A **declarative sentence** makes a statement. It ends with a period. (.)	Monsters are due on Maple Street.
An **interrogative sentence** asks a question. It ends with a question mark. (?)	What is going on?
An **imperative sentence** gives a command. It ends with a period or an exclamation point. (. or !)	Do not leave town. Watch out!
An **exclamatory sentence** calls out or exclaims. It ends with an exclamation point. (!)	Hey! How frightened we were!

Note that the subject of an imperative sentence is always the word *you*, and it is never stated: *(You) do not leave town. (You) watch out!*

Also note that in your writing, you should use exclamatory sentences as if they were a powerful spice. For the greatest effect, use them sparingly.

A. DIRECTIONS: *Add the correct endmark to each sentence. Then, identify the sentence as* declarative, interrogative, imperative, *or* exclamatory.

1. Where did you go on your field trip on Saturday _____ _____

2. We drove to a quarry and looked for fossils _____ _____

3. What cool fossils _____ _____

4. This one is a trilobite _____ _____

5. Don't drop it _____ _____

6. Next time we go, you should come with us _____ _____

7. Will you tell me when you plan to go again _____ _____

B. Writing Application: *Write a short dialogue between two characters. Use at least one of each kind of sentence. Label your sentences* dec *for declarative,* int *for interrogative,* imp *for imperative, and* exclam *for exclamatory.*

_____

_____

_____

_____

"The Monsters Are Due on Maple Street" by Rod Serling
Selection Test A

Critical Reading *Identify the letter of the choice that best answers the question.*

____ 1. In Act I of "The Monsters Are Due on Maple Street," which event signals the beginning of the town's troubles?

    A. A woman's telephone does not work.

    B. A man's electric mower will not start.

    C. A roar is heard, and a flash of light is seen.

    D. A boy tells about some stories he has read.

____ 2. In Act I of "The Monsters Are Due on Maple Street," what motivates Steve to explain the flash of light by talking about meteors and sunspots?

    A. He knows a lot about science and wants to educate his neighbors.

    B. He wants to reassure himself that there is nothing to fear.

    C. He is from outer space and wants to act like a human being.

    D. He wants to find the meteor and sell it to a collector.

____ 3. In Act I of "The Monsters Are Due on Maple Street," Tommy makes some suggestions about the events that are causing fear on Maple Street. Which suggestions does he make?

    I.   People from outer space are responsible.

    II. Some people on Maple Street are from outer space.

    III. Mr. Goodman is from outer space.

    IV. Nobody should try to leave the town.

    A. I, II, IV

    B. II, III, IV

    C. I, III, IV

    D. I, II, III

____ 4. In Act I of "The Monsters Are Due on Maple Street," what is Steve's motivation for asking Tommy to explain his story about the aliens sent ahead to earth?

    A. He wants to make Tommy look foolish.

    B. He wants to know what Tommy thinks.

    C. He wants to take charge of the action.

    D. He wants to leave town immediately.

___ 5. Which of these events in Act I of "The Monsters Are Due on Maple Street" is a clue that the neighbors will stop trusting one another?

A. Don suggests that an electrical storm has caused the power to go off.

B. A woman says that Tommy has been reading too many comic books.

C. A man says that they should not be paying attention to Tommy.

D. Steve jokes that they should check to see who among them is human.

___ 6. Which of these details would not be important in a summary of the action of Act I of "The Monsters Are Due on Maple Street"?

A. Pete Van Horn is tall and thin.

B. Electric appliances stop working.

C. Neighbors wonder who among them is an alien.

D. Tommy says that no one should leave town.

___ 7. Which of these is the best summary of Act I of "The Monsters Are Due on Maple Street"?

A. The neighbors on Maple Street are unhappy because their power is out.

B. Les Goodman frightens his neighbors when his car starts by itself.

C. A strange event causes neighbors to become suspicious of one another.

D. Pete Van Horn leaves Maple Street to see what is happening elsewhere.

___ 8. In Act II of "The Monsters Are Due on Maple Street," what role does Steve play as his neighbors keep watch on the Goodmans' house?

A. He acts as the hanging judge: He tries to convince them that Goodman is dangerous.

B. He acts as executioner: He volunteers for a firing squad to execute the guilty parties.

C. He acts as peacemaker: He tries to persuade his neighbors to put aside their suspicions.

D. He acts as spy: He tries to reach the aliens on his ham radio.

___ 9. What emotion motivates Steve in this speech from Act II of "The Monsters Are Due on Maple Street"?

Go ahead, what's my wife said? Let's get it all out. Let's pick out every idiosyncrasy of every single man, woman, and child on the street. And then we might as well set up some kind of kangaroo court. How about a firing squad at dawn, Charlie, so we can get rid of all the suspects?

A. disgust

B. amusement

C. sorrow

D. love

___ 10. Which statement best summarizes the theme of "The Monsters Are Due on Maple Street"?

    A. Good neighbors should not object to being observed by the police.

    B. When neighbors suspect one another, they can destroy their community.

    C. Neighborhoods should be prepared for an invasion from outer space.

    D. If everyone is suspected of being dangerous, then no one is dangerous.

___ 11. Who or what are the monsters in the title "The Monsters Are Due on Maple Street"?

    A. the people who live on Maple Street

    B. the electric appliances on Maple Street

    C. Les and Ethel Goodman

    D. Figures One and Two

Vocabulary and Grammar

___ 12. In which sentence is the meaning of the word *flustered* suggested?

    A. That was the way they prepared things for the landing.

    B. He always was an oddball. Him and his whole family.

    C. I don't understand. I swear . . . I don't understand.

    D. They pick the most dangerous enemy they can find.

___ 13. Which of these sentences is declarative?

    A. It was an eventful night on Maple Street.

    B. Was it an eventful night on Maple Street?

    C. Observe the eventful night on Maple Street.

    D. What an eventful night it was on Maple Street!

Essay

14. In Act I of "The Monsters Are Due on Maple Street," after he has heard Tommy's story about the aliens, Steve makes this comment:

> Well, I guess what we'd better do then is to run a check on the neighborhood and see which ones of us are really human.

In an essay, discuss two emotions that might have motivated Steve to make that comment.

15. The stage directions at the end of "The Monsters Are Due on Maple Street" note that Figures One and Two cannot be clearly seen. If you were directing the play, would you depict the figures as aliens, as monsters, or as human beings? In an essay, describe how you would depict the figures, and explain the reasons for your choice. Include one detail from the play to support your explanation.

"The Monsters Are Due on Maple Street" by Rod Serling
Selection Test B

Critical Reading *Identify the letter of the choice that best completes the statement or answers the question.*

_____ 1. Which event in "The Monsters Are Due on Maple Street" starts the breakdown of the community?
  A. the voices of Figure One and Figure Two
  B. the sound of an object passing overhead
  C. an argument between Steve and Charlie
  D. a story told by Tommy about space aliens

_____ 2. In Act I of "The Monsters Are Due on Maple Street," what motivates Steve to identify meteors and sunspots as the source of the neighborhood's troubles?
  A. He is an astronomy teacher.
  B. He is an alien disguised as a human.
  C. He wants to reassure the neighbors.
  D. He wants to excavate the meteor.

_____ 3. In Act I of "The Monsters Are Due on Maple Street," at what point do the neighbors begin to consider the possibility that one of them is responsible for the strange events?
  A. when Pete Van Horn says that he is going to see if the power is still on on Floral Street
  B. when Tommy says that aliens resembling humans are sent ahead to prepare for a landing
  C. when Steve talks about meteors and sunspots as the most likely explanation
  D. when Steve and Charlie decide that they will walk downtown to talk to the police

_____ 4. Which of these details is unimportant to a summary of Act I of "The Monsters Are Due on Maple Street"?
  A. Phones and various machines stop working.
  B. A large object flashes overhead and disappears.
  C. Steve has recently filled his car's gas tank.
  D. Tommy says that no one should leave the town.

_____ 5. What emotion motivates Steve to make this speech in Act II of "The Monsters Are Due on Maple Street"?

  There's something you can do, Charlie. You could go home and keep your mouth shut. You could quit strutting around like a self-appointed hanging judge and just climb into bed and forget it.

  A. optimism
  B. fury
  C. love
  D. boredom

___ 6. Which of these statements would be unimportant in a summary of Act I?
   A. A roar and a flash of light interrupt the usual events in a neighborhood one evening.
   B. The power fails, telephones and portable radios do not work, and cars will not start.
   C. A boy says that the aliens would not like it if the neighbors left the town.
   D. A man reminds his neighbors that his family has lived on the street for five years.

___ 7. In Act II of "The Monsters Are Due on Maple Street," why are the residents so quick to focus on one another as the source of their fear?
   A. They have never trusted one another.
   B. They want to keep the focus off themselves.
   C. They have evidence that there are aliens in the town.
   D. They see that some neighbors have lights and some do not.

___ 8. Which detail from Act II of "The Monsters Are Due on Maple Street" is essential to an understanding of the play?
   A. Sally says that she and Ethel Goodman have been friends for years.
   B. Steve says that no one may enter his home without a search warrant.
   C. Charlie believes that Pete Van Horn is a monster and shoots him.
   D. The lights in Charlie's house suddenly come back on.

___ 9. What emotion motivates the speakers in this passage from Act II of "The Monsters Are Due on Maple Street"?

   WOMAN. [*In a very hushed voice*] Charlie . . . Charlie . . . the lights just went on in your house. Why did the lights just go on?

   DON. What about it, Charlie? How come you're the only one with lights now?

   GOODMAN. That's what I'd like to know.

   A. suspicion
   B. anger
   C. sympathy
   D. despair

___ 10. At the climax of "The Monsters Are Due on Maple Street," what single message underlies all of the characters' statements?
   A. Pick on them, not on me!
   B. I want my lights back on!
   C. I never believed in aliens!
   D. Somebody, call the police!

___ 11. What can you conclude from the dialogue between Figures One and Two at the conclusion of "The Monsters Are Due on Maple Street"?
   A. This is not the first town they have visited.
   B. They know how to control meteors and sunspots.
   C. They will settle on Maple Street as human beings.
   D. They are successful only in small towns.

____ 12. Which of these lines best expresses the theme of "The Monsters Are Due on Maple Street"?
    A. "I was just tryin' to . . . tryin' to protect my home, that's all!"
    B. "Maybe Peter there was trying to tell us something."
    C. "No . . . no . . . it's nothing of the sort! I don't know why the lights are on."
    D. "They pick the most dangerous enemy they can find . . . and it's themselves."

____ 13. What two things does the narrator compare in the final passage of "The Monsters Are Due on Maple Street"?
    A. meteors and sunspots
    B. bombs and prejudices
    C. explosions and fallout
    D. neighbors and outsiders

Vocabulary and Grammar

____ 14. In which sentence is the meaning of the word *sluggishly* suggested?
    A. My brother shuffled into the room and slumped into a chair.
    B. Her aunt prepared for the tournament by working out every day.
    C. His sister worked at her computer until she had finished her paper.
    D. The adventurers rafted through the dangerous white-water rapids.

____ 15. In which sentence is the meaning of the word *defiant* suggested?
    A. Well, why don't you go downtown and check with the police.
    B. Go ahead, Tommy. What kind of story was this?
    C. It's just a ham radio set. A lot of people have them.
    D. If they want to look inside our house—let them get a search warrant.

____ 16. Which of these sentences is imperative?
    A. Operator, operator, something's wrong on the phone, operator!
    B. Well, why don't you go downtown and check with the police.
    C. Come over here and stop that kind of talk.
    D. Charlie, there's a dead man on the sidewalk and you killed him!

Essay

17. When the neighbors begin to suspect Charlie in "The Monsters Are Due on Maple Street," he runs toward his house, and the neighbors chase him. Charlie then declares that the "monster" is Tommy. In an essay, explain why Charlie makes this accusation. Then, explain why the neighbors are ready to believe him.

18. As you were reading "The Monsters Are Due On Maple Street," what did you think had caused the mysterious events—the roar and the flash, the power outage, the dead phones and radios, the cars that would not start and then started on their own? In an essay, describe what you believed was the cause of the events. When you read the end of the play, when the space craft and vaguely seen figures are described, what did you think? Did the ending change your ideas? Why or why not?

from **Our Town** by Thornton Wilder
"My Head Is Full of Starshine" by Peg Kehret
Vocabulary Warm-up Word Lists

Study these words from the selections. Then, complete the activities.

Word List A

appetite [AP i tyt] *n.* desire for food
  The smell of my grandmother's cooking always gives me an <u>appetite</u>.

decent [DEE suhnt] *adj.* good or satisfactory
  Louise's silk dress was the only <u>decent</u> thing she had to wear to the party.

disturb [dis TURB] *v.* to annoy someone or interrupt what they are doing
  I try not to <u>disturb</u> my mother while she is paying the bills.

expensive [eks PEN siv] *adj.* costing a lot of money
  Ben had to save for months to buy a pair of <u>expensive</u> running shoes.

fines [FYNZ] *n.* money paid as a punishment for doing something wrong
  The driver had to pay $150 in <u>fines</u> for parking illegally.

items [EYE tuhmz] *n.* single things in a set
  Among the <u>items</u> on the menu were several unusual appetizers, such as snails.

notices [NOH tis iz] *n.* printed or written announcements
  Maggie put up <u>notices</u> all around the school to announce the Winter Dance.

practical [PRAK ti kuhl] *adj.* sensible or showing good judgment
  The committee liked our <u>practical</u> suggestions for amending the dress code at school.

Word List B

abruptly [uh BRUPT lee] *adv.* suddenly, unexpectedly
  The train stopped <u>abruptly</u> when the engineer saw a cow on the tracks.

according [uh CAWRD ing] *prep.* as shown or said by someone
  <u>According</u> to the weatherman, the rain will stop tomorrow.

advance [ad VANS] *n.* ahead of time; before an anticipated event
  We ordered our tickets for the concert in <u>advance</u> to make sure we got good seats.

critical [KRIT i kuhl] *adj.* very important
  This research phase of the project is <u>critical</u> to its success.

emotion [ee MOH shuhn] *n.* strong human feeling, such as love or hate
  The death scene in the play caused Alison to tremble with <u>emotion</u>.

faults [FAWLTS] *n.* weaknesses in someone's character
  We must not judge other people because we all have our <u>faults</u>.

misery [MIZ uh ree] *n.* great suffering or unhappiness
  After the hurricane, Jeb felt only a life of <u>misery</u> lie ahead of him.

potential [puh TEN shuhl] *n.* natural ability that could be developed
  With a little more training, Nancy has the <u>potential</u> to become an effective manager.

from Our Town by Thornton Wilder
"My Head Is Full of Starshine" by Peg Kehret
Vocabulary Warm-up Exercises

Exercise A *Fill in each blank in the paragraph below with an appropriate word from Word List A. Use each word only once.*

Using one of the library computers was a(n) [1] _____ decision

for Joyce. Her dad used the family computer during the day and it was too

[2] _____ to buy another one. Joyce discovered that the library

was a(n) [3] _____ place to work. It was quiet. There was no one to

[4] _____ her. When she needed to stretch, she would walk around

and read the [5] _____ on the bulletin boards. Some of the

[6] _____ on the boards were interesting. She could use the reference

books without checking them out, saving overdue [7] _____. The only

down side was the "no food in the library" rule. Somehow, knowing she couldn't eat

increased her [8] _____, so when she got home she ate like a horse!

Exercise B *Answer the questions with complete explanations.*

Example: If you have the <u>potential</u> to accomplish something worthwhile, would your
teacher discourage you from trying it?
   *If I had the <u>potential</u> to do something worthwhile, my teacher would probably
   encourage me because I have the ability to do it.*

1. If you make restaurant reservations <u>in advance</u>, is it likely you will wait for a table?
   _____

2. If you play <u>according to</u> the rules of the game, is your opponent likely to get angry?
   _____

3. If someone constantly reminds you of your <u>faults</u>, are you likely to remain friendly
   with that person?
   _____

4. If you are experiencing a strong <u>emotion</u>, is it likely you are bored?
   _____

5. If someone is living in <u>misery</u>, is it likely he or she is enjoying life?
   _____

6. If you are <u>abruptly</u> interrupted during an oral report, are you likely to be upset?
   _____

7. If an action is <u>critical</u> to your plan, is it likely you would avoid doing it?
   _____

Name _____ Date _____

from **Our Town** by Thornton Wilder
"My Head Is Full of Starshine" by Peg Kehret
Reading Warm-up A

Read the following passage. Pay special attention to the underlined words. Then, read it again, and complete the activities. Use a separate sheet of paper for your written answers.

Janie and Deanne decided to start a fund-raising club for local charities. Janie, the <u>practical</u> one, made notes as she and Deanne brainstormed ways to encourage kids to attend the first meeting.

Deanne, the creative one, had already thought of a name, *The Buzz Club.* She liked that name because the club offered opportunities to exchange ideas and work for the community. She suggested the members called themselves the Bees, but Janie nixed that idea. "Boys will never go for it, and most girls will think it's corny, too."

"I don't think it's corny," Deanne retorted. "Each member could wear a gold pin shaped like a bee or a hive."

"Gold pins would be <u>expensive</u> for a lot of kids. Let's discuss it at our first meeting." Janie glanced down the <u>items</u> on her "TO DO" list. "Where should we meet?"

"The Juice Bar on 8th Street is a <u>decent</u> place. They have big tables. Also, I like the idea of meeting in a café because talking gives me an <u>appetite</u>."

Janie thought a moment. "Would it <u>disturb</u> the owner?"

"Mr. Geary? Oh, he won't mind. He's a really nice guy. I think he'd be glad to see us there."

"I don't know," Janie thought aloud. "The idea of meeting in a café makes me nervous. Some kids might not come if they think they have to buy something."

"Well, there's a meeting room in the public library. We don't need money to use the library except to pay <u>fines</u> for overdue books."

"True," Janie agreed. "Now, we'll need to make <u>notices</u> telling people when and where to go for the first meeting."

"I'll do that," Deanne offered. "I've got some great ideas for decorating the notices."

Janie sighed. "Okay, but please, no bees!"

Deanne laughed. She wondered how two such opposite people could be such great friends!

1. Circle the name of the <u>practical</u> friend. Write about one way in which you are *practical*.

2. Circle the words that tell what may be <u>expensive</u>. Rewrite the sentence using a synonym for *expensive*.

3. Underline the words that tell where the <u>items</u> appeared. List two *items* that might appear there.

4. Underline the words that tell which place is <u>decent</u>. Describe a café that is *decent*.

5. Circle the words that tell who the meeting might <u>disturb</u>. Give a synonym for *disturb*.

6. Circle the word that tells what gives Deanne an <u>appetite</u>. Write about something that gives you an *appetite*.

7. Underline the words that tell what kind of <u>fines</u> you pay in a library. Name some other kinds of *fines*.

8. Underline the words telling the purpose of the <u>notices</u>. Write headlines for two *notices*, announcing the meeting.

Name _____ Date _____

from **Our Town** by Thornton Wilder
"My Head Is Full of Starshine" by Peg Kehret
Reading Warm-up B

Read the following passage. Pay special attention to the underlined words. Then, read it again, and complete the activities. Use a separate sheet of paper for your written answers.

According to the writer Somerset Maugham, "There are three rules for writing a novel. Unfortunately, no one knows what they are." In other words, writing is a complicated and highly individual art. If you have ever faced the misery of a blank page awaiting your thoughts, you know how difficult it is to write a convincing thank-you note, never mind an original story. Most writers do agree, however, that to write well, a person must follow at least three rules: (1) have something to say, (2) stick to the point, and (3) be truthful. Any writer who has potential but lacks experience will take these rules to heart.

Having something to say requires thinking time. Many writers think about a story idea for months before they begin to write. During this time they continually ask themselves questions. What are the main character's strengths and faults? What does the character want, and what is standing in the way? How can this obstacle be overcome, and why does it matter? From the answers to these and many other questions, a plot begins to emerge. The writer knows what story to tell.

Once the writing begins, the writer must stick to the point, which is why it is critical to know in advance what the story is about. Some writers work out the ending of the story before they begin to write. They then make sure every event moves toward the desired ending. If an event is not important to the outcome, out it goes.

The truth of a story lies in the honesty of its message. The message may reveal what it means to be a friend, or how to get through tough times, or how good often triumphs over evil. The message is never abruptly stated; instead, it rises out of the story like an emotion rises out of the body. If the message is true, the reader is left with a satisfying feeling. Most writers learn how to write truthfully by reading good books. Another way is to write from the heart.

1. Underline the name of the writer the rules are according to. Write the meaning of *according* to.

2. Underline the words that tell what kind of misery you may have faced as a writer. Give an antonym for *misery*.

3. Circle the words that tell who may have potential. Underline the nearby word that tells what else a writer needs. Explain why you need both, using *potential* in your answer.

4. Circle the word that means the opposite of faults. Write a sentence using the word *faults*.

5. Underline the words that tell what is critical. Write the meaning of *critical*.

6. Circle a word that means the same as in advance. Write about something you do in *advance* of something else.

7. Circle the word that tells what is never abruptly stated. Rewrite the sentence using a synonym for *abruptly*.

8. Circle the words that tell from where an emotion rises. Write about something that fills you with *emotion*.

Name _____ Date _____

from Our Town by Thornton Wilder
"My Head Is Full of Starshine" by Peg Kehret
Literary Analysis: Comparing Dramatic Speeches

Dramatic speeches are performed by actors in a drama or play. Whether spoken by a single character or as part of a larger scene, these speeches move the action of the story forward and help define the conflict within the plot. There are two main types of dramatic speeches:

- **Monologues** are long, uninterrupted speeches that are spoken by a single character. They reveal the private thoughts and feelings of the character.
- **Dialogues** are conversations between characters. They reveal characters' traits, develop conflict, and move the plot along.

Our Town is a dialogue, and "My Head Is Full of Starshine" is a monologue. As you read those selections, consider how you learn about the characters. Also, think about the ways in which other key information is revealed.

DIRECTIONS: *Answer the following questions about the excerpt from* Our Town *and "My Head Is Full of Starshine."*

1. In the excerpt from *Our Town,* what does the audience learn about George's character?

   _____

   _____

2. How does the audience learn this information?

   _____

3. What does the audience learn about Emily's character?

   _____

   _____

4. How does the audience learn this information?

   _____

5. How does Pam seem to view the speaker in "My Head Is Full of Starshine"?

   _____

   _____

6. What is Pam like? Why are the descriptions of Pam and the speaker important?

   _____

   _____

7. What does the speaker say about herself?

   _____

   _____

Name _____ Date _____

from **Our Town** by Thornton Wilder
"My Head Is Full of Starshine" by Peg Kehret
Vocabulary Builder

Word List

conceited	practical	rummaging	potential

A. DIRECTIONS: *Read each sentence, paying attention to the italicized word from the Word List. Then, answer each question, and explain your answer.*

1. If you accidentally threw away a diamond ring, might you be *rummaging* through the trash?

_____

2. Is a *practical* person one who daydreams and puts things off until the last minute?

_____

3. Is someone likely to be selfless, caring, and *conceited*?

_____

4. Is someone with great *potential* as an athlete likely to compete in the Olympics someday?

_____

B. DIRECTIONS: *Write the letter of the word whose meaning is* most like *that of the word from the Word List.*

_____ 1. conceited
    A. humble   B. sticky   C. realistic   D. vain

_____ 2. practical
    A. happy   B. realistic   C. strong   D. imaginative

_____ 3. rummaging
    A. reselling   B. organizing   C. searching   D. destroying

_____ 4. potential
    A. capability   B. intelligence   C. sharpness   D. volume

Name _____   Date _____

from **Our Town** by Thornton Wilder
"My Head Is Full of Starshine" by Peg Kehret
Support for Writing to Compare Dramatic Speeches

Use this graphic organizer to take notes for your essay comparing and contrasting the dramatic speech by Emily in the excerpt from *Our Town* with the one by the speaker in "My Head Is Full of Starshine."

Which ideas in the speech are familiar to you?_____
_____
_____
_____

With which ideas in the speech do you agree or disagree? _____
_____
_____
_____

Which character do you relate to more? Why?
_____
_____
_____
_____
_____
_____

The speaker in "My Head Is Full of Starshine"

Emily in *Our Town*

Which character do you think you learn more from? Why? _____
_____
_____
_____
_____
_____

Which ideas in the speech are familiar to you? _____
_____
_____
_____

With which ideas in the speech do you agree or disagree? _____
_____
_____
_____

Now, use your notes to write a draft of an essay comparing and contrasting the two speeches.

from **Our Town** by Thornton Wilder
"My Head Is Full of Starshine" by Peg Kehret
Selection Test A

Critical Reading *Identify the letter of the choice that best answers the question.*

____ 1. In the excerpt from *Our Town*, what does George ask Emily when he is carrying her books home?
   A. "Why aren't we friends anymore?"
   B. "Why are you mad at me?"
   C. "Why do you ignore me?"
   D. "Why are you crying?"

____ 2. In the excerpt from *Our Town*, why has Emily been treating George differently?
   A. She thinks he has become conceited.
   B. She has begun to like him.
   C. She no longer likes him.
   D. She wants them to be just friends.

____ 3. In the excerpt from *Our Town*, where does George ask Emily to go during their walk home?
   A. to the school dance
   B. to visit him at college
   C. to study in the library
   D. to get an ice-cream soda

____ 4. What does the following line from *Our Town* reveal about George's character?
   I'm celebrating because I've got a friend who tells me all the things that ought to be told me.
   A. He has many good and honest friends.
   B. He admires Emily for telling the truth.
   C. He likes people who praise him.
   D. He is not easily hurt by criticism.

____ 5. In these lines from *Our Town*, what does the audience learn about George?
   No, Emily, you stick to it. I'm glad you spoke to me like you did. But you'll see: I'm going to change so quick—you bet I'm going to change.
   A. He can change his mind about things quickly.
   B. He is promising to change only so that Emily will write to him.
   C. He truly cares what Emily thinks of him.
   D. He is not conceited, but he wants to make Emily feel better.

_____ 6. What aspect of the excerpt from *Our Town* makes it a dialogue?

    A. It is a conversation between characters.

    B. It is written in the form of a play.

    C. The characters' actions are described.

    D. The characters' thoughts are described.

_____ 7. According to the speaker in "My Head Is Full of Starshine," what does Pam mean when she says that the speaker's head is "full of starshine"?

    A. The speaker is ridiculous, and Pam wishes she would change.

    B. The speaker's poetry makes no sense.

    C. The speaker needs to concentrate harder.

    D. The speaker is different from her, and Pam does not mind that.

_____ 8. According to the speaker in "My Head Is Full of Starshine," what does she do to get ready for Margo's party while Pam has been preparing a dress for the party?

    A. choosing the outfit she will wear

    B. writing a poem for Margo

    C. working to pay for Margo's gift

    D. studying to improve her grade in science

_____ 9. According to the speaker in "My Head Is Full of Starshine," what assignments does she love?

    A. studying insects

    B. reading about flying carpets

    C. writing essays or stories

    D. studying the behavior of animals

_____ 10. According to the speaker in "My Head Is Full of Starshine," why does she pretend that her chair is a flying carpet during science class?

    A. She does not like what the teacher is talking about.

    B. She has a hard time paying attention in any class.

    C. She does not like her science teacher.

    D. She wants to visit other countries.

_____ 11. What does the speaker in "My Head Is Full of Starshine" mean by this remark, which she makes at the end of the monologue?

    My head is full of starshine. Except for those library fines, I'm glad it is.

    A. She likes herself the way she is, for the most part.

    B. She plans to remember to return her books on time.

    C. She is glad that she is able to see stars at night.

    D. She likes writing, but she does not like reading.

____ 12. What aspect of "My Head is Full of Starshine" makes it a monologue?

    A. It is about only one topic.

    B. It is about one person's life.

    C. It characterizes only one person.

    D. It is spoken by one character.

Vocabulary

____ 13. In which sentence might a character be said to be working up to her *potential*?

    A. Pam makes a list of everything she plans to do the next day.

    B. Pam pays attention in science class and gets an A for the term.

    C. The speaker in "My Head Is Full of Starshine" forgets to return library books on time.

    D. The speaker in "My Head Is Full of Starshine" daydreams during science class.

____ 14. If someone is *rummaging* through a box, what is he or she doing?

    A. destroying the contents

    B. crinkling the contents

    C. organizing the contents

    D. looking through the contents

____ 15. Which sentence best describes someone who is *conceited*?

    A. George offers to carry Emily's books home from school.

    B. George does not speak to people who are less popular than he.

    C. Emily tells George what she thinks is wrong with him.

    D. Emily apologizes to George for criticizing his behavior.

Essay

16. Both Emily in the excerpt from *Our Town* and the speaker in "My Head Is Full of Starshine" give dramatic speeches. In an essay, compare and contrast Emily's speech to George with the opening of "My Head Is Full of Starshine," in which the speaker compares Pam's preparations for a party with her own preparations. Tell why each speaker is giving the speech and what you learn about each speaker from the speech.

17. A monologue is a long speech given by one character; a dialogue is a conversation between two or more characters. In an essay, contrast the extract from *Our Town* with "My Head Is Full of Starshine." Tell which selection is a dialogue and which is a monologue. Then, explain how you can tell the difference between the two. Finally, tell which selection you preferred, and explain why.

Name _____ Date _____

from **Our Town** by Thornton Wilder
"My Head Is Full of Starshine" by Peg Kehret
Selection Test B

Critical Reading *Identify the letter of the choice that best completes the statement or answers the question.*

_____ 1. In the excerpt from *Our Town*, why does George offer to carry Emily's books home for her?
A. Her books are heavy.
B. She has a long walk home.
C. He likes her friend Lizzy.
D. He wants to talk to her alone.

_____ 2. In the excerpt from *Our Town*, why does Emily find it difficult to tell George what she thinks?
A. She believes that what she has to say is mean.
B. She likes George and does not want to hurt him.
C. She is afraid that George will get mad at her.
D. She is not telling George the truth.

_____ 3. What do you learn about Emily's character in these lines from *Our Town*?
I don't like the whole change that's come over you in the last year. I'm sorry if that hurts your feelings, but I've got to tell the truth . . .
A. She is unsure of herself.
B. She is judgmental and harsh.
C. She has a hard time confronting people.
D. She will not lie to spare someone's feelings.

_____ 4. In the excerpt from *Our Town*, what does Emily say to explain to George why she has been treating him differently lately?
A. He has become conceited.
B. She has not had time to talk to him.
C. He has hurt her feelings by dating other girls.
D. She no longer likes him and has been afraid to tell him.

_____ 5. In the excerpt from *Our Town*, how does George react to Emily's assessment of his behavior?
A. He accepts it and thanks her for her honesty.
B. He accepts it but feels bitter toward her.
C. He does not agree with her but treats her kindly.
D. He does not agree with her and gets angry.

_____ 6. In the excerpt from *Our Town*, what does the stage manager reveal, and how?
A. By fixing the ice-cream sodas, he reveals that he knows that George likes Emily.
B. By asking why Emily has been crying, he reveals that she is upset.
C. By asking why Emily has been crying, he reveals that George is conceited.
D. By talking about Main Street, he reveals that he is not paying attention to Emily.

____ 7. What aspect of the excerpt from *Our Town* makes it a dialogue?
  A. The stage manager assumes the role of one of the characters.
  B. There is a conflict between George and Emily.
  C. Emily gives George her honest opinion of his behavior.
  D. It consists of a conversation between several characters.

____ 8. According to the speaker in "My Head Is Full of Starshine," how does Pam feel about her?
  A. Pam feels annoyed with her because she is scatterbrained and dreamy.
  B. Pam thinks that she is foolish because she writes meaningless poetry.
  C. Pam likes her because she, like Pam, is practical and well organized.
  D. Pam accepts her as a friend even though she is different from Pam.

____ 9. According to the speaker in "My Head Is Full of Starshine," what is practical about Pam?
  A. She makes a list of everything she needs to do the next day.
  B. She says that the speaker's head is "full of starshine."
  C. She is interested in ladybugs.
  D. She gets A's in science.

____ 10. In "My Head Is Full of Starshine," why does the speaker's mother wish the speaker were more like Pam?
  A. Unlike Pam's room, her room is always messy.
  B. She forgets to bring notices home from school.
  C. Unlike Pam, she does poorly in science.
  D. She writes poetry instead of studying science.

____ 11. Why would Mr. Evans, the science teacher mentioned in "My Head Is Full of Starshine," prefer Pam as a student to the speaker?
  A. Pam collects ladybugs and sells them to fruit growers.
  B. Pam always earns A's, whereas the speaker earns B's and C's.
  C. Pam is writing a paper on the magic mud in Kansas City.
  D. Pam pays attention and finds the lessons fascinating.

____ 12. What does this line from "My Head Is Full of Starshine" reveal about the speaker?
  When Mr. Evans talks about gross things like that, I pretend my chair is a flying carpet, and I watch myself float out the window.

  A. The speaker does not like Mr. Evans.
  B. The speaker is more creative than scientific.
  C. The speaker has always been a poor student.
  D. The speaker likes fairy tales.

____ 13. Why does the speaker in "My Head Is Full of Starshine" describe her friend Pam?
  A. Pam is her best friend.
  B. She longs to be more like Pam.
  C. Pam's differences help to reveal her character.
  D. She is annoyed with Pam because she is so different from her.

___ 14. What aspect of "My Head Is Full of Starshine" makes it a monologue?
   A. It is a long, uninterrupted speech spoken by a single character.
   B. It is spoken without any enthusiasm, in a dull tone of voice.
   C. It consists of a comparison of the speaker and another character.
   D. It is a dramatic speech that moves the action of the story forward.

Vocabulary

___ 15. Which of the following characters is most likely *conceited*?
   A. Richard is always quick to offer praise, encouragement, or sympathy.
   B. Julie is friends with people whose interests are different from hers.
   C. John volunteers at a soup kitchen every Sunday morning.
   D. Mary is friends only with people who, like her, are on the honor roll.

___ 16. Which of the following characters is most obviously *practical*?
   A. Amanda is extremely funny and would like to be a stand-up comedian someday.
   B. Jose plans his menus ahead of time and makes a list of the ingredients he needs.
   C. Lisa began assembling her new lawn mower without reading the instructions.
   D. Evan helped Lisa with the lawn mower instead of studying for his science exam.

___ 17. Who would most likely be *rummaging*?
   A. someone who is late for a date
   B. someone who is planning a party
   C. someone who is organizing something
   D. someone who is looking for something

Essay

18. In an essay, define a monologue and a dialogue, and then tell which of the two selections the excerpt from *Our Town* and "My Head Is Full of Starshine" is a monologue and which is a dialogue. Cite two details from each work that help to characterize it as one kind of dramatic speech or the other.

19. Both the excerpt from *Our Town* and "My Head Is Full of Starshine" are about friendship. In an essay, compare the friendship between George and Emily with the friendship between the speaker in "My Head Is Full of Starshine" and Pam. What is the conflict in each friendship? How is it resolved? Conclude your essay by telling which friendship you preferred reading about and explaining why.

Name _____ Date _____

Writing Workshop—Unit 5, Part 2
Exposition: Cause-and-Effect Essay

Prewriting: Narrowing Your Topic

Use the following web to narrow your topic. Write your topic in the center, surround it with subtopics, and list causes and effects connected to each subtopic.

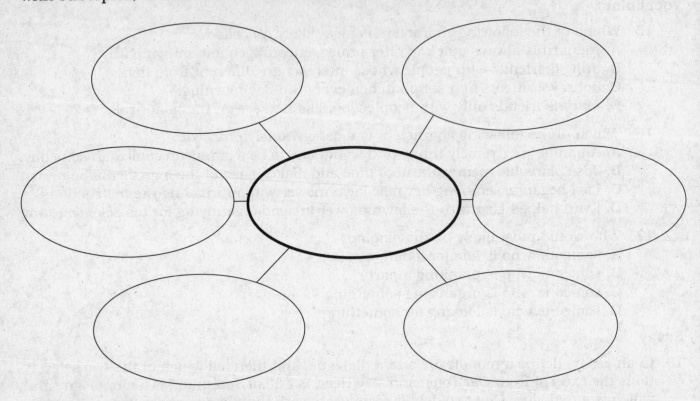

Drafting: Organizing Your Essay

List the main points of your cause-and-effect essay in the following graphic organizer.

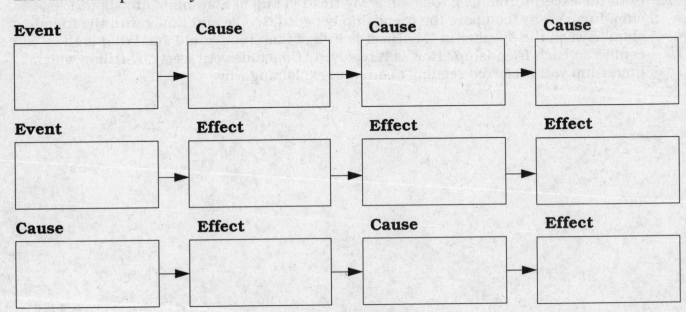

Name _____ Date _____

Cause-and-Effect Essay: Integrating Grammar Skills

Revising for Subject-Verb Agreement with Compound Subjects

A verb must agree with its subject in **number**.

Singular Subject and Verb: A *battery comes* with the music player.

Plural Subject and Verb: Two *batteries come* with the music player.

Two or more subjects joined by *and* are plural in number and require a plural verb:

Plural Subject and Verb: Two *batteries and a plug come* with the music player.

Subjects joined by *or* and *nor* are considered singular unless the *last* part is plural.

Singular Subject and Verb: Either a *battery or a plug comes* with the music player.

Singular Subject and Verb: Either two *batteries or a plug comes* with the music player.

Plural Subject and Verb: Either a *plug or* two *batteries come* with the music player.

Identifying Correct Subject-Verb Agreement

A. DIRECTIONS: *Complete each sentence by circling the verb that agrees with the subject.*

1. Hot peppers and tomatoes (combines, combine) for a tasty hot sauce.
2. Supermarkets or smaller Mexican groceries (sells, sell) many varieties.
3. Neither my mom nor my sisters (likes, like) my favorite sauce.
4. Either Baton Rouge or New Orleans (produces, produce) a special hot sauce.
5. Two small bottles or a bigger jar (is, are) on my shopping list.

Fixing Incorrect Subject-Verb Agreement

B. DIRECTIONS: *On the lines provided, rewrite these sentences so that they use correct subject-verb agreement. If a sentence is correct as presented, write correct.*

1. Milk and cheese often comes from Wisconsin and Vermont.

   _____

2. Neither Wisconsin nor Vermont produce as much beef as Texas.

   _____

3. Either Brazil or Argentina are known for beef.

   _____

4. Neither Australia nor the British Isles has as many cows as Canada.

   _____

Name _____ Date _____

Vowel Sounds in Unstressed Syllables

The vowel sounds in many words can be hard to hear, which then makes the word hard to spell. This usually happens in **unstressed,** or **unaccented, syllables.** Notice how the *i* in *disease* sounds the same as the *ai* in *captain*. This unclear vowel sound can occur in more than one syllable and can be spelled in a number of different ways.

Word List

amusing	bulletin	disease	sensitive	vertical
attorney	captain	quotient	sponsor	vitamin

A. DIRECTIONS: *On the line, write the word in parentheses that is correctly spelled.*

1. a good source of (vitemin, vitamin) C _____

2. the (quotent, quotient) of a division problem _____

3. called his (atterney, attorney) for advice _____

4. (sensitive, sensative) feelings that are often hurt _____

5. a ten-foot (vertical, verticle) drop _____

6. pinned a note on the (bullitin, bulletin) board _____

7. needed a (sponser, sponsor) for our project _____

8. an (amusing, emusing) cartoon _____

9. met the (captain, captin) of the ship _____

10. a bad skin (desease, disease) _____

B. DIRECTIONS: *Write two sentences using each group of words below.*

1. *bulletin, amusing,* and *vertical*

_____

_____

_____

2. *sensitive, disease, vitamin,* and *attorney*

_____

_____

_____

3. *captain, sponsor,* and *quotient*

_____

_____

_____

Name _____ Date _____

Evaluating Media Messages

After choosing your commercial, fill out the following chart to evaluate the effects and techniques of what you see.

Title of commercial: _____

What are some of the images presented in the commercial?

What is the message behind them?

What mood is created by the sound effects or music?

What techniques are used to persuade you to agree with this message?

How would you rate the credibility of this message?

Name _____ Date _____

For Further Reading—Unit 5

DIRECTIONS: *Think about the books you have read. Then, on a separate sheet of paper, answer the discussion questions and take notes for your literary circle.*

A Christmas Carol by Charles Dickens

Discussion Scrooge and the Ghost of Christmas Present visit several places other than the Cratchits' house. Name three of these places. Explain what these places have in common.

Connections: Literature Circle Scrooge does something on Christmas Day that surprises his nephew, Fred. What does Scrooge do? How does Fred react to it? What new insight has Scrooge gained from his experiences with the ghosts?

A Tale of Two Cities by Charles Dickens

Discussion How does Dickens characterize Charles Darnay in Chapter 2? What hints in this chapter suggest that he will be developed as a romantic hero?

Connections: Literature Circle What is symbolic about Miss Pross's meeting place with Jerry Cruncher for their final escape?

Don't Tell Anyone by Peg Kehret

Discussion In the **narrative structure** of this novel, the author tells about the car accident from Lacey's point of view and then tells about it again from Megan's point of view. How do you think Megan's point of view will affect Lacey's situation?

Connections: Literature Circle What **theme,** or general insight, do Lacey's actions suggest about the importance of honesty and responsibility? Use examples from this work, other literature, history, science, and your own experience to support your ideas during discussion.

The Mousetrap by Agatha Christie

Discussion Identify two red herrings, or false clues, meant to mislead us about the murderer's identity and so add to the mystery.

Connections: Literature Circle Were you fooled about the murderer's identity? Was he the "least likely suspect," as sometimes happens in mysteries? Explain.

Name _____ Date _____

Unit 5: Drama
Part 2 Benchmark Test 10

MULTIPLE CHOICE

Reading Skill: Summarizing *Read the selection. Then, answer the questions that follow.*

[1] Lydia Kamakameha was born in 1838 into a high-ranking family in Hawaii. In her twenties, she married the son of a Boston sea captain. When Lydia's brother died in 1891, Lydia became queen of Hawaii and was given the royal name Queen Liliuokalani. As queen, she strongly favored Hawaii's independence and actively fought against annexation of her beloved islands by the United States.

[2] Nonnative Hawaiians with businesses in the islands opposed the queen because she refused to recognize special rights and privileges for their businesses. In 1893, Liliuokalani was dethroned as a result of her refusal and temporarily put under house arrest. After her public life, Liliuokalani wrote songs and books about Hawaii. She composed "Aloha Oe," one of the best-known Hawaiian songs. Queen Liliuokalani died in 1917, in Honolulu, Hawaii.

1. Which of the following is the least important detail in paragraph 1?
   A. Lydia was given the name Liliuokalani.
   B. Lydia's husband was the son of a sea captain.
   C. The queen favored Hawaii's independence.
   D. Liliuokalani did not want Hawaii annexed to the United States.

2. Which of the following would be important in summarizing the selection?
   A. knowing something about the author
   B. analyzing an author's purpose
   C. identifying important ideas in the selection
   D. relating what you know to the selection

3. Which of these is the best summary of paragraph 1?
   A. Lydia Kamakameha was born into a high-ranking family and married the son of a sea captain in her twenties.
   B. As Queen Liliuokalani, the former Lydia Kamakameha fought for Hawaiian independence.
   C. Lydia Kamakameha was born in 1838 and became queen when her brother died, in 1891.
   D. When she succeeded her brother as ruler of Hawaii, Liliuokalani fought to keep Hawaii independent.

4. Which information from paragraph 2 would you include in a summary of the selection?
   A. The queen was dethroned in 1893.
   B. The queen was put under house arrest.
   C. The queen died in Honolulu, Hawaii.
   D. "Aloha Oe" is a well-known song.

5. Which of the following is the best summary of paragraph 2?
   A. Non-native Hawaiians wanted to keep special rights and privileges, but the queen opposed them.
   B. Dethroned in 1893 for opposing rights for non-native businesses, the queen retired to write until her death, in 1917.
   C. After being deposed, the queen wrote books and songs about Hawaii, one of which became well-known.
   D. Some business owners opposed the queen and were able to get her dethroned, in 1893.

Read the selection. Then, answer the questions that follow.

[1] Who else but a group of scientists would watch a group of dolphins blowing bubbles and start to ask questions? Researchers at Six Flags Marine World, in California, were observing young bottlenose dolphins as they blew bubbles under water. The dolphins sometimes made bubble rings by expelling air through their blow holes. As a bubble ring rose, a dolphin would bat at it with a fin. Then, before the ring reached the water's surface, the dolphin would bite the ring to pop it.

[2] Are dolphins able to plan ahead? The scientists who studied the dolphins' bubble-making think this might be true. They noticed that if a dolphin's first bubble ring was well-formed, the dolphin was more likely to make a second ring. The two rings usually combined to make a large ring that was even more fun to flip and pop. If the first ring wasn't a good one, though, the dolphin wouldn't bother to make another one. It was as if the dolphin were saying, "Why bother?"

6. Which detail from paragraph 1 is important for a summary of the selection?
   A. Six Flags Marine World is in California.
   B. Researchers are studying bottlenose dolphins.
   C. Scientists are studying dolphins' bubble-blowing.
   D. Dolphins expel air through their blow holes.

7. Which information from paragraph 2 could be omitted without changing the meaning of the selection?
   A. Scientist think that dolphins may plan ahead.
   B. If the first ring was well-formed, a dolphin blew another one.
   C. The dolphin seemed to say, "Why bother?"
   D. The larger ring was more fun to flip and pop.

8. Which of the following is the best one-sentence summary of the selection?
   A. Scientists think that dolphins' bubble-blowing might show that they can plan ahead.
   B. Dolphins often blow a second bubble, if the first one is well-formed.
   C. If dolphins blow a bubble that is not well-formed, they are not likely to blow a second one.
   D. One way that dolphins play is to blow bubble rings through their blow holes.

9. Which of the following requires careful reading?
   A. skimming a magazine article
   B. scanning for unfamiliar words
   C. reading a comic strip
   D. completing a job application

10. If you are completing a form for a volunteer position at a library, why should you read each word of the form carefully?
    A. to find out if the library will share your information with others
    B. to learn more about the work of library volunteers
    C. to determine whether you would enjoy the work
    D. to make sure that you fill out every section correctly

Literary Analysis: Characters' Motives *Read the selection. Then, answer the questions that follow.*

In a small town there lived a poor shoemaker and his daughter, Sophia. One day, as the shoemaker approached the town with a wagonload of new shoes, a wealthy merchant stopped him and asked, "How much for everything?" The shoemaker named a fair price, which the merchant accepted. Then, the merchant climbed in the wagon and claimed it, saying, "You agreed to sell me 'everything,' didn't you? That includes your wagon and horse."

When Sophia heard about this, she had an idea. The next day, she loaded some shoes in a wheelbarrow and went to town. When the merchant saw her, he asked, "How much for everything?" He reached into his pocket and produced three copper pieces. Sophia said she would take everything in his hand. When the merchant agreed, Sophia then told him that "everything" included the merchant's fine ring on his hand. Sophia offered to trade the ring for her father's wagon and horse. Realizing that he'd been tricked, the merchant agreed. And so Sophia returned home with her father's horse and wagon, and three copper pieces as well.

11. Which of the following best defines *characters' motives*?
   A. persons or animals in a literary work
   B. the reasons for characters' actions
   C. the process of creating characters
   D. the traits of characters

12. Which word best states the main motive of the merchant in this story?
   A. power
   B. greed
   C. jealousy
   D. anger

13. Why does Sophia go to town?
   A. She wants to give the merchant his money back.
   B. She wants to buy goods from the merchant.
   C. She wants to sell more shoes in the market.
   D. She wants to get her father's wagon and horse back.

14. What is the merchant's reason for giving Sophia the horse and wagon?
   A. He feels guilty for tricking her father.
   B. Sophia has paid him a fair price.
   C. He wants to keep his ring.
   D. He wants to make a fair trade.

Literary Analysis: Comparing Dramatic Speeches *Read the selections. Then, answer the questions that follow.*

Speech 1:

When I look at our community library, I realize what people can accomplish by working together. I'm remembering how Ms. Hannah and Mr. Floyd suspended their decades-long feud to work together to raise money for the library. I am reminded of times when my family and friends encouraged me to complete a different task. By ourselves, we can't do much; together, we're more powerful than we imagine.

Speech 2:

Marcus. The thing is, we've got to look out for ourselves. You just can't depend on others.

Aisha. Why do you say that?

Marcus. Because it's true. People will always let you down.

Aisha. I disagree. You're being unfair.

Marcus. I'm being realistic. For instance, when I asked Jeff to help me with a science project, he was too busy. When Tim agreed to be my jogging partner, he broke his ankle.

15. Which of the following best describes Speech 1?
    A. dialogue
    B. monologue
    C. narration
    D. dialect

16. Which of the following is a characteristic of a dramatic speech?
    A. It is a long speech by a main character.
    B. It moves the action of a story forward.
    C. It usually involves two characters.
    D. It resolves a conflict in a drama.

17. Which of the following best describes the speaker in Speech 1?
    A. humble and admiring of others
    B. full of self-importance
    C. too eager to give others credit
    D. ambitious and self-confident

18. Which of the following best describes Marcus in Speech 2?
    A. eager to find fault in others
    B. unwilling to admit mistakes
    C. practical and sensible
    D. lacking faith in others

Vocabulary: Suffixes

19. What is the meaning of *patriotic* in the following sentence?

    Mr. Callas's patriotic yard display included a large plastic Statue of Liberty.

    A. causing national pride
    B. characterized by loyalty
    C. pertaining to love of one's country
    D. the study of citizenship

20. What is the meaning of *realize* in the following sentence?

    Vanessa would soon realize her dream of publishing an original song.

    A. to make actual
    B. pertaining to reality
    C. able to accomplish
    D. the result of effort

21. What is the meaning of *scientific* in the following sentence?

Ms. Nguyen used a scientific approach to finding the cause of the leak.

   A. one who uses the methods of science   **C.** pertaining to science

   B. the result of technology   **D.** the product of factual knowledge

22. What is the meaning of *criticize* in the following sentence?

Emil squinted thoughtfully at the artwork, and then began to criticize its every aspect.

   A. a type of examination   **C.** relating to an object's worth

   B. to make a judgment   **D.** a state of being judged

23. What is the meaning of *poetic* in the following sentence?

At dinner, Carson delivered a poetic tribute to his father's tuna casserole.

   A. one who writes verse   **C.** to create a poem

   B. resembling a poet   **D.** pertaining to poetry

24. What is the meaning of *civilize* in the following sentence?

Huck Finn feared that his aunt would try to civilize him.

   A. to make better behaved   **C.** the result of civil action

   B. pertaining to courtesy   **D.** the state of being improved

Grammar: Sentence Functions and End Marks

25. Which of the following sentences is a command?
   A. Do you enjoy gospel music?   **C.** What an amazing sunset!
   B. Please lock the door when you leave.   **D.** Cattle drives were long and difficult.

26. Which category best describes the following sentence?

Can kangaroos walk on all four legs?

   A. declarative   **C.** imperative
   B. interrogative   **D.** exclamatory

27. Which of the following sentences uses correct end punctuation?
   A. Give me your unwanted shoes?   **C.** Run for your life.
   B. Did you see the glassblower.   **D.** Those waves are awesome!

Grammar: Revising for Subject-Verb Agreement of Compound Subjects

28. What is the best way to correct the following sentence?

Swimming and baseball is my favorite sports.

   A. Change *and* to *or*.   **C.** Change *is* to *are*.
   B. Change *is* to *were*.   **D.** Change *sports* to *sport*.

29. Which sentence has correct subject-verb agreement?
    A. A train or a bus provide a hands-free way to travel.
    B. Taking deep breaths or going for a walk helps the body relax.
    C. Either Sally or Jessica know how to operate this machine.
    D. Cities or states pays for local public libraries.

30. In which sentence do the subjects and verb agree?
    A. Both cats and dogs sometimes gets fleas.
    B. Neither Philip nor Angie wants to cancel the show.
    C. Automobiles and factories creates smog.
    D. Smoke or steam are rising from the neighbor's house.

Spelling: Plurals

31. Which sentence has the correct plural form of *journey*?
    A. The explorers kept notes on their many journies.
    B. How many journeyes did Columbus make to America?
    C. The settlers' journeys West took many months.
    D. Kellerman became lost on the first of several journys to Africa.

32. Which sentence has the correct plural form of *goose*?
    A. Nine geese flew in formation overhead.
    B. E. B. White kept several gooses.
    C. The goose were loud and ill-mannered.
    D. I startled two geeses near the pond.

33. Which sentence has the correct plural form of *waltz*?
    A. Johann Strauss wrote many waltzs.
    B. The dancers performed three waltzes.
    C. I cannot name many waltzies.
    D. Viennese waltzses are light and airy.

ESSAY

Writing

34. Suppose that the mayor of your town has asked you to write a report on conditions in your neighborhood. In particular, the mayor would like to know your recommendations for changes that would improve the neighborhood. On a separate sheet of paper, write a paragraph in which you describe (1) how you will gather information for the report; (2) how you will organize the report; and (3) two or more recommendations for changes that you might include.

35. Think of at least four topics for a cause-and-effect essay. On a separate sheet of paper, jot down the topics. Then, choose the one topic that most interests you. Write a sentence and tell why the topic is interesting to you. Finally, list at least three questions you hope to answer in your essay.

36. Think of an occurrence in nature that interests you. For example, you might be interested in finding out more about lightning or hibernation. Imagine that you are preparing to write a cause-and-effect essay on this occurrence. In order to narrow your topic, draw a topic web on a separate sheet of paper. First, draw a circle in the center of your page. Then, write the topic inside the circle. Next, write at least four connected ideas or questions inside new circles around your topic. Draw lines connecting these ideas to the main topic.

ANSWERS

from *Dragonwings* by Laurence Yep

Vocabulary Warm-up Exercises, p. 2

A. 1. contraption
2. demonstration
3. haul
4. audience
5. serious
6. repeat
7. steep
8. flight

B. Sample Answers

1. Egg yolks and egg whites might be *separated* so that the egg whites could be beaten for a special recipe.

2. If I *expected* to win a special award, I might prepare an acceptance speech.

3. Two *machines* I might use at home would be a vacuum cleaner and a garbage disposal.

4. An *immigration* officer makes sure that people coming into the United States have permission to do so.

5. If I dropped my clothes off at a *laundry*, I would want them to be washed and ironed or folded.

6. To earn money, *merchants* sell or trade things.

7. If Alex says he will *probably* go to a party, there is a good chance he will be there, but it is not certain.

8. The last time I got sick, it took me three days to *recover*.

Reading Warm-up A, p. 3

Sample Answers

1. Besides you and the Wrights, four men and a boy are there to witness this demonstration.; The last time I was part of an *audience*, I saw a basketball game.

2. see if they will actually fly this time, witness; The *demonstration* proved that the kite could fly quite high.

3. (aeroplane); Nobody had ever seen such a strange *contraption*.

4. flat; I would rather climb a *steep* hill because it is more of a challenge.

5. (to the sand bar at Kitty Hawk); The last time I had to *haul* something heavy from one place to another was when I moved my dresser to the other side of my room.

6. 12 seconds; 120 feet; *Flight* means "relating to the act or manner of flying."

7. (the plane needs major repairs); I hurt my wrist playing volleyball, but the injury was not *serious*.

8. the experiment; *Repeat* means "to do over again."

Reading Warm-up B, p. 4

Sample Answers

1. the war; If I were trying to *recover* from a disappointment, I might try to stay busy with things that would distract me.

2. (to work for very little pay); I *expected* Marie to join me for lunch on Wednesday.

3. they were welcomed at first; *Immigration* means "coming to a foreign country to live there."

4. (they worked hard), (they kept to themselves); This is *most likely* because they worked hard and kept to themselves.

5. their families; Jennie *separated* the blue beads from the yellow beads.

6. (people who didn't want to wash and iron their own clothes); I might find shirts, slacks, and other things that need washing and ironing at a *laundry*.

7. produce manufactured goods; *Machines* are "mechanical devices or equipment."

8. (shopkeepers and traders); The *merchants* on Sutter Street sell a variety of products.

Laurence Yep

Listening and Viewing, p. 5

Sample answers and guidelines for evaluation:

Segment 1. Laurence Yep read science-fiction stories because the characters were taken to different worlds and had to learn new customs and languages. Students should provide a reasonable explanation for their reaction to Yep's interest in science fiction. Most likely, they will say that they are not surprised because science fiction is exciting, or they may draw a connection between Yep's background as a Chinese American growing up in two cultures and the experiences of characters in science fiction, who often encounter cultures other than their own.

Segment 2. Yep points out that novels contain more detail than dramas and build a complete world for the reader. Dramas sketch the background and provide a strong physical and emotional presence. Students should provide a reasonable explanation for their choice of the more difficult genre to write. They may suggest that a drama would be more difficult because the story must be told largely through dialogue. Alternatively, they may say that it would be more difficult to write a novel because it is so long that it might easily become boring.

Segment 3. Yep continuously rewrites to add details and layers to his original story. Students may suggest that, like Yep, they would do research to gather background material, set a schedule to be productive, or rewrite to add details and "layers."

Segment 4. Yep believes that books can open doors. They can take readers to new places, give them new experiences, and show them that they are not alone.

Unit 5: Learning About Drama, p. 6

A. 1. It is a kitchen at 7 A.M. There is a table, at least one chair, and a door.

2. The props are a newspaper and a book bag.

3. "almost shouting" *or* "patiently"

4. "rushes in" *or* "getting up from the table"

5. It is dialogue, a conversation between two characters. There are no long speeches.

6. Students will probably say that it seems to be from a comedy because it involves normal characters, and one has made a humorous mistake.

from *Dragonwings* by Laurence Yep

Model Selection: Drama, p. 7

A.
1. The setting is Piedmont, outside a stable.

2. Moon Shadow is most likely using paper and a pen or pencil.

3. Guidelines for evaluation: Sound effects include a cough as the motor starts, the roar as the propellers turn, the roar of the plane in flight, and a gong at the end of the scene.

4. The speech is a monologue. It is long speech involving only a single character, and it reveals the character's thoughts.

5. Sample answer: The main character is Moon Shadow. He appears at the beginning of the scene and again at the end. The events seem to be told from his point of view, and he reveals his thoughts in a monologue.

B. Students should recognize that the climax occurs when the airplane takes off. They should recognize that Windrider realizes that when he was flying, Moon Shadow seemed to be disappearing from his life; he realizes that he must give up flying and dedicate himself to his family. Although Moon Shadow is the main character, his insights in response to the flight are not clearly articulated. Students should note that by appearing as an adult in the cap his father gives him after the failed flight and by referring to never-forgotten dreams, he shows that in some way his father's dream of flying has had an important influence on his life.

Selection Test A, p. 8

Learning About Drama

1. ANS: C	DIF: Easy	OBJ: Literary Analysis
2. ANS: C	DIF: Easy	OBJ: Literary Analysis
3. ANS: B	DIF: Easy	OBJ: Literary Analysis
4. ANS: B	DIF: Easy	OBJ: Literary Analysis
5. ANS: D	DIF: Easy	OBJ: Literary Analysis
6. ANS: A	DIF: Easy	OBJ: Literary Analysis

Critical Reading

7. ANS: B	DIF: Easy	OBJ: Literary Analysis
8. ANS: D	DIF: Easy	OBJ: Comprehension
9. ANS: C	DIF: Easy	OBJ: Comprehension
10. ANS: A	DIF: Easy	OBJ: Comprehension
11. ANS: B	DIF: Easy	OBJ: Comprehension

12. ANS: D	DIF: Easy	OBJ: Comprehension
13. ANS: D	DIF: Easy	OBJ: Interpretation
14. ANS: C	DIF: Easy	OBJ: Literary Analysis
15. ANS: C	DIF: Easy	OBJ: Comprehension

Essay

16. Students should recognize that Windrider is a dreamer. The monologue suggests that until now he has put his dreams ahead of his responsibilities as a father and husband, but the flight in the airplane has changed him, and now, he says, he wishes to fulfill his responsibilities. Students may refer to his decision to work for Uncle Bright Star in the laundry and bring Moon Shadow's mother from China.
Difficulty: Easy
Objective: Essay

17. Students should express some understanding of the importance of the dream of flying to Moon Shadow, or they might tie the line to Moon Shadow's apparent respect for and admiration of his father.
Difficulty: Easy
Objective: Essay

Selection Test B, p. 11

Learning About Drama

1. ANS: C	DIF: Average	OBJ: Literary Analysis
2. ANS: A	DIF: Average	OBJ: Literary Analysis
3. ANS: D	DIF: Challenging	OBJ: Literary Analysis
4. ANS: C	DIF: Challenging	OBJ: Literary Analysis
5. ANS: D	DIF: Challenging	OBJ: Literary Analysis
6. ANS: C	DIF: Average	OBJ: Literary Analysis

Critical Reading

7. ANS: A	DIF: Average	OBJ: Comprehension
8. ANS: C	DIF: Average	OBJ: Comprehension
9. ANS: B	DIF: Average	OBJ: Comprehension
10. ANS: D	DIF: Average	OBJ: Comprehension
11. ANS: C	DIF: Challenging	OBJ: Literary Analysis
12. ANS: B	DIF: Average	OBJ: Interpretation
13. ANS: D	DIF: Average	OBJ: Interpretation
14. ANS: A	DIF: Average	OBJ: Interpretation
15. ANS: C	DIF: Challenging	OBJ: Comprehension
16. ANS: B	DIF: Average	OBJ: Comprehension
17. ANS: A	DIF: Average	OBJ: Interpretation
18. ANS: D	DIF: Average	OBJ: Comprehension
19. ANS: D	DIF: Average	OBJ: Interpretation
20. ANS: D	DIF: Challenging	OBJ: Interpretation

Essay

21. Students should recognize that the cap in some way symbolizes the relationship between the father and his son. They may also associate it with the flight of the airplane or with the father's decision to give up flying, go to work for Uncle, and bring his wife from China. They should recognize that Moon Shadow wears the cap at the end of the scene, when he appears as an adult, to show that he respects and admires his father.

Difficulty: *Average*

Objective: *Essay*

22. Students should recognize that the ending provides a resolution: It allows the audience to know that Windrider never flies again, though he always dreamed of flying. They might also note that by giving Moon Shadow the final lines, the playwright brings the focus back to him, reminding the audience that he is the main character of the play.

Difficulty: *Average*

Objective: *Essay*

Unit 5, Part 1 Answers

Diagnostic Test 9, p. 15

MULTIPLE CHOICE

1. ANS: D
2. ANS: B
3. ANS: C
4. ANS: C
5. ANS: B
6. ANS: D
7. ANS: A
8. ANS: A
9. ANS: B
10. ANS: C
11. ANS: D
12. ANS: A
13. ANS: D
14. ANS: B
15. ANS: C

A Christmas Carol: Scrooge and Marley, Act I, by Israel Horovitz

Vocabulary Warm-up Exercises, p. 19

A. 1. gold
2. perfection
3. miser
4. shrivels
5. penance
6. lustrous

7. resolute
8. replenish

B. Sample Answers

1. *establishments/businesses;* Many businesses flourish in the downtown area.
2. *welfare/well-being;* After the hurricane hit, the well-being of the residents was a big concern.
3. *impropriety/misbehavior;* So impolite was the audience's misbehavior that they talked during the performance.
4. *bleak/cold;* The cold winter landscape did not look inviting.
5. *grindstone/millstone;* The team worked as hard as mules pulling a millstone.
6. *surviving/still-living;* The still-living family members gathered for a reunion.
7. *neglected/ignored;* The ignored needs of the less fortunate were not being met.

Reading Warm-up A, p. 20

Sample Answers

1. (hoarded all his valuables); A *miser* does not like to share his or her belongings with others.
2. shiny, yellow; Things made of *gold* might include coins or jewelry.
3. (his supply of gold); *Replenish* means "to make full again by supplying a new stock."
4. the brilliant, lustrous metal; *Perfection* to me is a beautifully written poem or a delicious ice cream sundae.
5. (brilliant); The *lustrous* sunshine made everything glow in its yellow light.
6. without food and drink, he could not live; *Shrivels* means "wrinkles or becomes withered."
7. determined; *Resolute* means "unwavering or determined."
8. (his greed); He wanted to do something to make up for his mistaken behavior in being a greedy miser.

Reading Warm-up B, p. 21

Sample Answers

1. hopeless; Some other things that might be *bleak* are cold, cloudy weather or the feeling people might have when coping with the aftermath of a hurricane that has caused much damage.
2. (boarding schools); The agency set up many *establishments* to help meet the needs of the voters.
3. (if one or both parents had died); *Surviving* means "still living or existing."
4. Children were often mangled by machinery. The shops were dismal, dirty places to work. The children toiled for long hours. They were powerless to rebel against these terrible conditions.; *Welfare* is "well-being."
5. dirty places to work; The *dismal* cabin was dark and dank.

6. (As a result of working long hours); "Noses to the grind-stone" means to always be working very hard. The expression comes from a millstone, also called a grind-stone, which is continuously in operation.

7. <u>if they were seen or heard around the family for whom they worked.</u>; *Impropriety* means "improper action or behavior."

8. (the basic needs of many children at work, school, and home); *Neglected* means "ignored or not properly cared for."

A Christmas Carol: Scrooge and Marley, Act I, by Israel Horovitz

Reading: Preview a Text to Set a Purpose for Reading, p. 22

1. The play is set in offices, homes, and other locations in London.

2. The play takes place on Christmas Eve, Christmas Day, and the day after Christmas in 1843.

3. **Sample answers:** to learn about a subject, to learn what life was like in England in the mid-nineteenth century, to gain understanding, to find out what people thought and valued at that time

4. They are dressed for warmth in old-fashioned clothing.

5. **Sample answers:** to learn about a subject, to gain understanding

6. **Sample answer:** to be entertained

Literary Analysis: Dialogue, p. 23

1. Three characters are speaking: Scrooge, a "portly" man, and a "thin" man.

2. **Sample answer:** Scrooge is rude, ungenerous, unpleasant, self-serving, and arrogant.

3. **Sample answer:** Scrooge is harsh—he believes that people should accept the help offered by the establishments he supports. When the do-gooders suggest that many poor people cannot or will not go to those places, he suggests that those people deserve to die and that the society would be better off without them. The do-gooders apparently believe that the well-off are obliged to try to help the poor.

4. the thin man or the portly man

Vocabulary Builder, p. 24

A. Sample answers follow each yes or no designation:

1. No, he asked with great intensity; *implored* means "begged."

2. No, he disliked celebrations; *morose* means "gloomy."

3. No, the *destitute* are poverty-stricken.

4. No, he saw nothing; *void* means "emptiness."

5. Yes, he has; *conveyed* means "made known."

6. No, during his lifetime, Marley was not known for his kindness.

B. 1. C; 2. D; 3. A; 4. D; 5. A; 6. C

Enrichment: Social Services, p. 27

A. 1. Students might find the information they need at *www.fns.usda.gov/fsp/*. In a phone directory, they should look in the section that lists county or state agencies (sometimes called the blue pages), under Department of Social Services.

2. Students might begin their research at *www.salvationarmyusa.org* or look in a phone directory. They might also look in the yellow pages of a phone directory, under the heading "Social and Human Services."

3. Students should go to *www.redcross.org* or look up the agency in a phone directory.

4. Students might look in the blue or yellow pages of a phone directory or do an Internet search.

5. Students should provide information about an organization in their community that performs a social service. They should name the sponsor and describe its mission.

B. Students should describe the reaction they would expect Scrooge to have to one of the organizations they researched in part A of this activity. They should provide a well-reasoned explanation in support of their opinion.

Build Language Skills: Vocabulary, p. 28

A. Sample Answers

1. We had to delete a paragraph to fix the alignment of the columns in the newsletter.

2. What is your assessment of the swimmer's chance of victory?

3. The witness will give a statement regarding what occurred on the night of the crime.

4. At the assembly tomorrow there will be an announcement regarding the winners of the spelling bee.

B. Sample answers follow the designation of each statement as true or false:

1. False; a groan would be the natural response to the loss of a championship game.

2. True; a teacher would want her students to participate in their schoolwork.

3. True; a conflict is a clash.

4. True; an assessment of a play would provide a good idea of what it is about.

5. False; an assumption is a guess; it is not a certainty.

Build Language Skills: Grammar, p. 29

A. Sample Answers

1. Oops, the cat spilled his food all over the floor.

2. Ouch! I dropped the hammer on my foot.

3. I worked for two hours in the hot sun. Whew!

4. Hmmm, I think this CD costs way too much.

5. Hey! Do not go near that downed electric wire.

B. Students should write three grammatically correct sentences, each containing an interjection and punctuated correctly.

Selection Test A, p. 30

Critical Reading

1. ANS: C	DIF: Easy	OBJ: Reading
2. ANS: C	DIF: Easy	OBJ: Reading
3. ANS: B	DIF: Easy	OBJ: Reading
4. ANS: C	DIF: Easy	OBJ: Interpretation
5. ANS: A	DIF: Easy	OBJ: Literary Analysis
6. ANS: B	DIF: Easy	OBJ: Literary Analysis
7. ANS: D	DIF: Easy	OBJ: Comprehension
8. ANS: B	DIF: Easy	OBJ: Interpretation
9. ANS: D	DIF: Easy	OBJ: Interpretation
10. ANS: A	DIF: Easy	OBJ: Interpretation
11. ANS: A	DIF: Easy	OBJ: Literary Analysis
12. ANS: A	DIF: Easy	OBJ: Interpretation

Vocabulary and Grammar

13. ANS: D	DIF: Easy	OBJ: Vocabulary
14. ANS: B	DIF: Easy	OBJ: Grammar

Essay

15. Guidelines for evaluation: Students should recognize the cynical and cantankerous attitude of Scrooge, who sees the holiday only as a time when he loses money, and the cheerful, generous attitude of the nephew, who sees the holiday as a time for goodwill and generosity.
Difficulty: *Easy*
Objective: *Essay*

16. Guidelines for evaluation: Students should recognize the similarities in the two men's lives. Scrooge may be influenced by Marley because they were equals—partners—at one time. In seeing Marley in chains, he has a sense of what awaits him if he does not reform.
Difficulty: *Easy*
Objective: *Essay*

Selection Test B, p. 33

Critical Reading

1. ANS: D	DIF: Average	OBJ: Reading
2. ANS: B	DIF: Average	OBJ: Reading
3. ANS: C	DIF: Average	OBJ: Reading
4. ANS: B	DIF: Average	OBJ: Comprehension
5. ANS: B	DIF: Challenging	OBJ: Literary Analysis

6. ANS: B	DIF: Average	OBJ: Literary Analysis
7. ANS: B	DIF: Challenging	OBJ: Interpretation
8. ANS: C	DIF: Challenging	OBJ: Interpretation
9. ANS: C	DIF: Challenging	OBJ: Interpretation
10. ANS: D	DIF: Challenging	OBJ: Comprehension
11. ANS: B	DIF: Average	OBJ: Literary Analysis
12. ANS: B	DIF: Challenging	OBJ: Literary Analysis

Vocabulary and Grammar

13. ANS: D	DIF: Average	OBJ: Vocabulary
14. ANS: A	DIF: Average	OBJ: Vocabulary
15. ANS: D	DIF: Average	OBJ: Grammar

Essay

16. Students may say that they have more sympathy for Scrooge now that they understand that as a child he was apparently sent away by his father and treated harshly by his schoolmaster and that as a young man he lost the woman he once loved. Alternatively, they may say that they have less sympathy for him because he was loved by his sister, liked by Fezziwig and Dick Wilkins, and loved by a woman but chose to dedicate his life to amassing wealth instead of enjoying friendship and love.
Difficulty: *Average*
Objective: *Essay*

17. Students should recognize that Marley is saying that he had misunderstood his business. He now realizes that instead of enriching himself, he should have been been working to improve humanity—by giving money to the poor, showing sympathy, having patience, and acting kindly. Students should justify this explanation by noting that Marley says that if people do not act in a positive manner during their lifetime, they are condemned to do so after they die—or, presumably, suffer consequences.
Difficulty: *Challenging*
Objective: *Essay*

A Christmas Carol: Scrooge and Marley, Act II, by Israel Horovitz

Vocabulary Warm-up Exercises, p. 37

A.
1. recollect
2. poem
3. thoughtful
4. fortune
5. heartily
6. praise
7. unaltered
8. value

B. Sample Answers

1. T; A *beggar* is someone who asks for charity, which means he or she does not have enough money to live properly.

2. T; Stealing is against the law, and if one is caught stealing, there will be a bad *consequence,* or "result of an action," such as being arrested and going to jail.

3. F; *Preserved* means "saved," and if we threw out the photos we did not save them.

4. F; If Brenda likes the smell, she does not think it is *odious,* which means "disgusting."

5. T; Most people like to be told to do something in a polite way, and *nasty* means "unpleasant."

6. F; *Workhouses* are poorhouses, where poor people who could not pay their debts were sent.

7. T; A *refuge* is a safe place to go, and if we don't have one then we cannot escape the storm.

8. T; A *resource* is something we can draw upon if needed, and if we are doing a big office project, the extra paper may come in handy.

Reading Warm-up A, p. 38

Sample Answers

1. (his past); A synonym for *recollect* is *remember.*

2. in money; Scrooge does not have a *fortune* in good values or kindliness.

3. (Scrooge); A *poem* is "a written piece that presents a powerful image or feeling and uses rhythmic or rhyming words."

4. When he realizes that few will ever miss him because of the sort of life he has lived; She became very *thoughtful* after reading the moving story.

5. (change); I would like our tradition of eating turkey on Thanksgiving to remain *unaltered.*

6. He brings good humor to all and generosity to those in need.; *Heartily* means "sincerely and fully."

7. sharing with others; I know the *value* of having my sister as a good friend.

8. (his generous actions); An antonym of *praise* is *criticize.*

Reading Warm-up B, p. 39

Sample Answers

1. the growth of more slums; *Consequence* means "a result of an action."

2. (because the government had no laws to protect them); The kind-hearted woman gave some food to the *beggars.*

3. (unclean); A synonym for *odious* is *disgusting.*

4. This was because they could be paid lower wages than men.; *Resource* means "something that can be drawn upon and used if needed."

5. the rights of children; The new law *preserved* the high standards for safe drinking water.

6. (the poor); *Workhouses* were different from the prisons because the poor were given jobs there to help provide

them with food and shelter. In the prisons, they were treated as criminals and locked up with other kinds of criminals.

7. conditions in the workhouses; I think it is *nasty* to have to look through garbage when I have mistakenly thrown away something valuable.

8. (Many poor); *Refuge* means "a safe place or shelter from danger."

A Christmas Carol: Scrooge and Marley, Act II, by Israel Horovitz

Reading: Adjust Your Reading Rate to Suit Your Purpose, p. 40

Sample Answers

1. I would read the dialogue quickly in order to create a feeling of conversation.

2. I would read the stage directions slowly and carefully, to look for information about action not revealed in the dialogue.

3. The stage directions reveal that the Ghost of Christmas Present sprinkles the two speakers with a substance. That action explains why the speakers suddenly treat each other respectfully.

4. I would read the passage slowly in order to reflect on the character's words and look for clues to the message.

Literary Analysis: Stage Directions, p. 41

1. Bob Cratchit and his son Tiny Tim

2. The "threadbare and fringeless comforter" indicates that the Cratchits are poor.

3. Tiny Tim wears leg braces and walks with the aid of crutches. He is light enough that his father easily bears him on his shoulders.

4. Scrooge and the Ghost of Christmas Future appear in this scene. The reader knows that Scrooge is there because he speaks. The reader knows that Christmas Future is there because his presence is announced in the stage directions.

5. The stage directions show that the setting changes. The Cratchits' home fades out, and a tombstone comes into view. Christmas Future points to the tombstone. Readers will therefore understand why Scrooge realizes at this moment that it was his own death that the businessmen, Old Joe, Mrs. Dilber, and the others were talking about.

Vocabulary Builder, p. 42

A. Sample answers follow each yes or no designation:

1. Yes, they will—*astonish* means "to amaze."

2. No, he cannot easily resist—a compulsion is an irresistible force.

3. No, she does not—*severe* means "harsh."

4. No, it was not—*meager* means "small in amount."

5. Yes, they can—*audible* means "loud enough to be heard."

B. 1. C; 2. D; 3. D; 4. A; 5. A

Enrichment: Holiday Observances, p. 45

A. Students should name a holiday and accurately answer the questions about that holiday, describing its meaning, the clothing typically worn on the holiday, the foods typically eaten during its observance, any places visited during its observance, any activities engaged in, and any other traditions relating to it.

B. Students should name their made-up holiday, describe its purpose, and describe traditions to be associated with it.

Build Language Skills: Vocabulary, p. 46

Sample Answers

A. 1. When I was younger, I had difficulty with subtraction.

2. Will there be a reduction in prices at the stores after the holidays?

3. Do not make the assumption that the weather will remain sunny all day.

4. Do you have a device for the detection of carbon monoxide in your home?

5. Can the team afford the addition of new uniforms to its budget?

B. 1. I had a strong reaction to the scary movie: The next night I had nightmares.

2. The philanthropist's enthusiasm for the project was evidence of his involvement in it.

3. The two characters' hostility was proof of their conflict.

4. After she saw the play, the critic wrote a critique pronouncing it a success.

5. Because we were not sure of all the facts about Dickens's life, we made an assumption about his character.

Build Language Skills: Grammar, p. 47

A. 1. ✗
2. ✓
3. ✓
4. ✗
5. ✗

B. Sample Answers

1. We do not have any bread for sandwiches.

2. The spy never had any intention of giving himself up.

3. This article does not have anything to do with our assignment.

4. They are not going to any championship game tonight.

5. Our dog will not ever eat any food she does not like.

Selection Test A, p. 48

Critical Reading

1. ANS: B	DIF: Easy	OBJ: Literary Analysis
2. ANS: D	DIF: Easy	OBJ: Interpretation
3. ANS: C	DIF: Easy	OBJ: Literary Analysis
4. ANS: C	DIF: Easy	OBJ: Interpretation
5. ANS: A	DIF: Easy	OBJ: Comprehension
6. ANS: C	DIF: Easy	OBJ: Comprehension
7. ANS: A	DIF: Easy	OBJ: Reading
8. ANS: A	DIF: Easy	OBJ: Interpretation
9. ANS: D	DIF: Easy	OBJ: Comprehension
10. ANS: B	DIF: Easy	OBJ: Reading

Vocabulary and Grammar

11. ANS: B	DIF: Easy	OBJ: Vocabulary
12. ANS: D	DIF: Easy	OBJ: Grammar

Essay

13. Students should recognize that in both instances, Scrooge visits families that are happy but not wealthy. In both cases, too, the wife believes Scrooge is a miser, whereas the husband defends him. Scrooge learns that happiness is more important than wealth, and for the first time he seems to care what people think of him—and is disturbed to find out that he is not universally well thought of.

Difficulty: *Easy*

Objective: *Essay*

14. Students should recognize that the Ghost of Christmas Future is frightening because he does not speak and because he shows Scrooge disturbing scenes—people talking about Scrooge's death, people who have stolen Scrooge's belongings after his death, and Scrooge's own gravestone.

Difficulty: *Easy*

Objective: *Essay*

Selection Test B, p. 51

Critical Reading

1. ANS: B	DIF: Challenging	OBJ: Interpretation
2. ANS: C	DIF: Average	OBJ: Literary Analysis
3. ANS: C	DIF: Challenging	OBJ: Literary Analysis
4. ANS: B	DIF: Average	OBJ: Reading
5. ANS: B	DIF: Average	OBJ: Literary Analysis
6. ANS: C	DIF: Average	OBJ: Reading
7. ANS: A	DIF: Average	OBJ: Comprehension
8. ANS: C	DIF: Average	OBJ: Interpretation

9. ANS: A   DIF: Average   OBJ: Interpretation
10. ANS: D   DIF: Challenging   OBJ: Interpretation

Vocabulary and Grammar

11. ANS: A   DIF: Average   OBJ: Vocabulary
12. ANS: D   DIF: Challenging   OBJ: Vocabulary
13. ANS: D   DIF: Challenging   OBJ: Grammar

Essay

14. In response to the first message, students should cite the effect that Scrooge's change has on the Cratchits, his nephew's family, and his community. In response to the second, they should refer to the meeting of the three businessmen and to the men and women who divide up Scrooge's possessions after his death. In response to the third message, they should cite Scrooge's giddiness as he buys gifts on Christmas Day, contributes to the poor, raises Bob Cratchit's salary, and so on.

    Difficulty: *Average*

    Objective: *Essay*

15. Students should describe Tiny Tim's leg braces and crutches. They might note that he is light enough to be carried by his father. They should refer to his musings at church and his selflessness. They might suggest that he is the focal point of his family and appears to represent goodness.

    Difficulty: *Average*

    Objective: *Essay*

from *A Christmas Carol: Scrooge and Marley,* Act I, Scenes 3 & 5 by Israel Horovitz

Vocabulary Warm-up Exercises, p. 55

A. 1. enormously
2. feast
3. suitors
4. compete
5. absolute
6. faintly
7. grace
8. gratitude

B. Sample Answers

1. No, *apprentices* usually receive room and board and instruction, not a salary, in return for working.
2. No, if it is *convenient* that means it is easily accomplished, so it would not take a long time.
3. Yes, if we are *bound* to run into a snowstorm, it means it will very likely happen, and therefore the trip may take longer than usual.
4. Yes, standing at *attention* means assuming a tall, standing posture and awaiting an order, which is a military custom.

5. No, most people like being treated with *dignity* because it means they are treated with respect and are held in high esteem.
6. No, if the person is a *master* that means he or she is very skilled at the job or is the boss, and probably knows a lot about the shop and the craft.
7. Yes, the room will probably grow darker because *snuffs* means "extinguishes," and when there is less light from a flame it gets darker in a room.
8. Yes, a person is likely to earn more *wages* by working more because wages are pay, and more pay is usually earned by working longer hours.

Reading Warm-up A, p. 56

Sample Answers

1. (holiday party); *Absolute* means "complete or whole."
2. Some dancers; When the runner sprinted, she ran with great *grace*.
3. (to see how many high kicks, fancy steps, and turns they could do); People may also *compete* in guessing games, soccer, or chess.
4. They stood by her side as they awaited a turn to dance with her.; *Suitors* are "men who are courting a woman."
5. (goose and beef), (tasty treats); I enjoy a *feast* of pizza with extra garlic and a salad.
6. The tasty treats; Synonyms for *enormously* are *greatly* and *immensely*.
7. The entire family sang carols.; The family's singing must have sounded loud and boisterous.
8. (for having such a fine family with whom to celebrate); *Gratitude* means "thankfulness."

Reading Warm-up B, p. 57

Sample Answers

1. cheap labor; *Bound* means "certain, sure, or having one's mind made up."
2. (to ask the workhouses to give them youngsters as apprentices); It is *convenient* to take a short cut to school because it makes the trip shorter.
3. (If a child became an apprentice, he or she would learn a trade, such as blacksmith or glass blower. The child would be given room and board in exchange for working for a master.); If I was an *apprentice*, I would like to learn how to make jewelry.
4. the owner or boss of the shop; One master was especially kind to his apprentices.
5. pay; I think it is unfair for anyone to be asked to work for no *wages*.
6. (treated the young workers with respect); *Dignity* means "the quality of being worthy of honor or respect."
7. ready to perform the next task required of them; Others who might stand at *attention* are military cadets.
8. (the youngsters' spirit was extinguished); *Snuffs* means "puts out or extinguishes a candle or something else."

Literary Analysis: Comparing Characters, p. 58

Sample Answers

1. *Scrooge* complains that Cratchit will want to take off Christmas Day and that Cratchit is picking his pocket by getting paid for the day. He asks Cratchit not to wish him a merry Christmas. *Fezziwig* orders his apprentices to stop working because it is Christmas Eve. He announces that they will have a party, orders a fiddler to play, and calls for his daughters.

2. *Scrooge* only complains. *Fezziwig* arranges a party, to which he invites his employees, his family, his daughters' "suitors," and others from the community; he laughs and dances.

3. *Scrooge* sees Christmas as an intrusion on his business. *Fezziwig* welcomes Christmas and celebrates it with generosity.

4. Cratchit indirectly reminds *Scrooge* that the next day is Christmas and teases him by wishing him a merry Christmas after Scrooge forbids him to do so. Dick Wilkins and the young Scrooge say that they are blessed to have a master like *Fezziwig*, and Scrooge promises that if he ever owns a business, he will treat his apprentices as well as Fezziwig treats them.

5. *Scrooge:* selfish, greedy, manipulative, mean; *Fezziwig:* happy, generous, kind

Vocabulary Builder, p. 59

A. Sample Answers

fiddler: Definition—person who plays a fiddle; *Synonym*—violinist; *Example sentence*—The fiddler played a waltz.

suitors: Definition—men who pay attention to women in the hopes of marrying them; *Synonyms*—beaus, boyfriends; *Example sentence*—The heiress had ten suitors, while her poor cousin had none.

Snuffs: Definition—puts out, as a candle; *Synonym*—extinguishes; *Example sentence*—My mother snuffs out candles with her fingers.

B. 1. C; 2. A; 3. D

Selection Test A, p. 61

Critical Reading

1. ANS: B	DIF: Easy	OBJ: Comprehension
2. ANS: A	DIF: Easy	OBJ: Comprehension
3. ANS: D	DIF: Easy	OBJ: Comprehension
4. ANS: B	DIF: Easy	OBJ: Interpretation
5. ANS: B	DIF: Easy	OBJ: Literary Analysis
6. ANS: C	DIF: Easy	OBJ: Comprehension
7. ANS: D	DIF: Easy	OBJ: Comprehension
8. ANS: D	DIF: Easy	OBJ: Comprehension
9. ANS: D	DIF: Easy	OBJ: Interpretation
10. ANS: A	DIF: Easy	OBJ: Literary Analysis
11. ANS: C	DIF: Easy	OBJ: Literary Analysis
12. ANS: A	DIF: Easy	OBJ: Literary Analysis

Vocabulary

13. ANS: D	DIF: Easy	OBJ: Vocabulary
14. ANS: A	DIF: Easy	OBJ: Vocabulary
15. ANS: C	DIF: Easy	OBJ: Vocabulary

Essay

16. Students should recognize that Scrooge is not a nice or an understanding employer. They should note that he does not provide adequate heat, he pays Cratchit a meager salary, and he resents giving him one paid day off a year. Students should state whether they would want to work for Scrooge and support their explanation with a detail from the excerpt.

Difficulty: *Easy*

Objective: *Essay*

17. Students should recognize that Fezziwig is Scrooge's opposite: He is kind and generous to his employees; he invites his employees, his servants, his family, his daughters' suitors—virtually everyone—to a Christmas party; he is fair and understanding. His apprentices appreciate and admire him. Students should state whether they would want to work for someone like Fezziwig and support their explanation with two details from the excerpt.

Difficulty: *Easy*

Objective: *Essay*

Selection Test B, p. 64

Critical Reading

1. ANS: C	DIF: Average	OBJ: Comprehension
2. ANS: C	DIF: Average	OBJ: Comprehension
3. ANS: B	DIF: Average	OBJ: Interpretation
4. ANS: D	DIF: Average	OBJ: Interpretation
5. ANS: C	DIF: Average	OBJ: Literary Analysis
6. ANS: D	DIF: Average	OBJ: Comprehension
7. ANS: D	DIF: Average	OBJ: Comprehension
8. ANS: B	DIF: Average	OBJ: Interpretation
9. ANS: D	DIF: Average	OBJ: Interpretation
10. ANS: A	DIF: Average	OBJ: Interpretation
11. ANS: D	DIF: Challenging	OBJ: Literary Analysis
12. ANS: D	DIF: Average	OBJ: Literary Analysis
13. ANS: A	DIF: Challenging	OBJ: Literary Analysis
14. ANS: B	DIF: Average	OBJ: Literary Analysis

Vocabulary

15. ANS: B   DIF: Average   OBJ: Vocabulary
16. ANS: B   DIF: Average   OBJ: Vocabulary
17. ANS: A   DIF: Average   OBJ: Vocabulary

Essay

18. Students should cite details showing that Scrooge is greedy and unkind while Cratchit is patient, sympathetic, and kind, and they should write a lucid, well-reasoned response to the question of which man they think would make the better boss.

    Difficulty: *Average*

    Objective: *Essay*

19. Students should note that the young Scrooge is happy, grateful, and friendly, whereas the older Scrooge is unhappy, ungrateful, and unfriendly; they should cite at least one detail from each scene to support their arguments.

    Difficulty: *Challenging*

    Objective: *Essay*

Writing Workshop—Unit 5, Part 1

Multimedia Report: Integrating Grammar Skills, p. 68

A. 1. beside; 2. except; 3. into; 4. advice; 5. effect

B. 1. correct

   2. I would advise you to go into the house before it rains.

   3. Many people besides me accept my mother's advice.

Unit 5, Part 1 Answers

Benchmark Test 9, p. 69

MULTIPLE CHOICE

1. ANS: B
2. ANS: A
3. ANS: D
4. ANS: C
5. ANS: A
6. ANS: B
7. ANS: A
8. ANS: A
9. ANS: D
10. ANS: A
11. ANS: B
12. ANS: C
13. ANS: B
14. ANS: C
15. ANS: A

16. ANS: D
17. ANS: C
18. ANS: B
19. ANS: B
20. ANS: A
21. ANS: D
22. ANS: D
23. ANS: C
24. ANS: D
25. ANS: C
26. ANS: D
27. ANS: B
28. ANS: D

ESSAY

29. Students' letters should express an opinion for or against the topic. They should include at least two main points, with supporting details. Each letter should include a salutation and a signature.

30. Students' tributes should be brief and should clearly state the qualities they admire in the people they write about. Each tribute should end with a concluding statement.

31. Students' paragraphs should express a clear topic for the report, with a description of the organizational plan and the types of media that will be used. Students should also describe the effects they hope to achieve with the various media.

Unit 5, Part 2 Answers

Diagnostic Test 10, p. 76

MULTIPLE CHOICE

1. ANS: C
2. ANS: C
3. ANS: A
4. ANS: B
5. ANS: B
6. ANS: B
7. ANS: C
8. ANS: C
9. ANS: D
10. ANS: D
11. ANS: B
12. ANS: B
13. ANS: A
14. ANS: A
15. ANS: C

"The Monsters Are Due on Maple Street"
by Rod Serling

Vocabulary Warm-up Exercises, p. 80

A. 1. afford
2. broadcast
3. hesitant
4. process
5. typical
6. Gradually
7. mildly
8. Obviously

B. Sample Answers

1. T; Few people have been able to reach the summit of Mount Everest, so it is an enormous, or *tremendous*, accomplishment indeed.
2. F; It wouldn't be fun to go camping in an area that is full of streets and homes.
3. F; You can never replace something that is *unique* because it is one of a kind.
4. F; It's not always fun to be around an *intense* person because he or she takes everything too seriously.
5. F; When you are in a hurry you are too distracted to be thoughtful and to think about things in a *reflective* way.
6. T; Dreams are a different level of consciousness in beyond normal time and space so you are in a different *dimension*.
7. T; If a horror movie is good, it will both scare and surprise the audience, so the *reaction* would be to scream with fright.
8. F; *Prejudices* are caused by fear and misinformation, so, if a person gets over his or her fear and becomes informed, he or she can overcome prejudices.

Reading Warm-up A, p. 81

Sample Answers

1. (televisions); *Afford* means "having enough money to buy something"
2. a big wooden box with a tiny 10-inch or 15-inch video screen; A *typical* TV set today has a flat screen measuring 25 to 50 inches wide. It can be free-standing or propped up on the wall.
3. (shows); Unfortunately, the shows were only slightly entertaining.
4. the screens got bigger. The picture improved, and so did the shows; Through practice, I am *gradually* becoming a better athlete.
5. the situation comedy, or "sitcom"; My favorite kind of *broadcast* is the reality show.
6. discontinuing black-and-white TVs and introducing color; I am in the *process* of completing my vocabulary assignment.

7. (eager); *Hesitant* means "unwilling to do something because you are unsure about it."
8. an unreal picture of real America; *Clearly*, TV changed people's lives.

Reading Warm-up B, p. 82
Sample Answers

1. There was no other show like it; Rod Serling was a writer with a *unique* voice.
2. lined with modest houses; A *residential* street in my area has old houses with great big yards and fences.
3. between dreams and imagination; They entered a *world* between dreams and imagination.
4. (thoughtful); I am usually feeling *reflective* at night when I lie awake thinking.
5. (introduction); My friend Jackie is an *intense* person who gets seriously involved in things that are important to her.
6. ideas and other people; People's *prejudices* against other people cause a lot of unhappiness.
7. (his shows), other TV shows of the time; A synonym for *tremendous* is *huge*.
8. audiences were ready for more thoughtful programs; *Reaction* means, "an action or feeling that is a response to something."

"The Monsters Are Due on Maple Street"
by Rod Serling

Reading: Distinguish Between Important and Unimportant Details to Write a Summary, p. 83

1. An out-of-the-ordinary event occurs, no one can explain it satisfactorily, and a boy starts talking about aliens.
2. The unnecessary detail is that Tommy wears eyeglasses.
3. The neighbors become suspicious of Les Goodman, and he says that they are letting a nightmare begin.
4. The unnecessary detail is that Goodman compares the neighbors to frightened rabbits. It is clear that it is unimportant because it is not necessary to an understanding of the play; the play would be complete and forceful without it.

Literary Analysis: A Character's Motives, p. 84

1. Steve may be motivated by confusion, fear, and a desire to find a reasonable explanation for the seemingly mysterious events.
2. Goodman
3. Don
4. anger and/or fear
5. Goodman is angry because his neighbors are acting as if he were responsible for the strange events. He may be frightened because he realizes that they are acting irrationally.

Vocabulary Builder, p. 85

A. Sample answers follow each yes or no designation:

1. No; a flustered person is nervous and so would not be likely to speak clearly.
2. No; a river would move quickly after a heavy rain.
3. Yes; someone who asks the same question firmly and steadily must be eager to know the answer.
4. Yes; a child who is boldly resisting would be likely to refuse to do his chores.
5. No; if the person has undergone a change, she is not likely to continue to be the way she used to be.

B. 1. B; 2. A; 3. C; 4. B; 5. D

Enrichment: Script Writing, p. 88

Students should describe a setting, two or more characters, and a science-fiction plot, including the conflict, the resolution, and a lesson that is conveyed by one of the characters.

Build Language Skills: Vocabulary, p. 89

A. 1. Alphabetize these names.
2. Jason worked hard to realize his dreams.
3. The scientists will analyze the evidence.
4. Can you memorize this poem?
5. The prairie dogs will colonize the plains.

B. Sample Answers

1. If you are arranging events in chronological order, you must begin with the oldest event and work forward, in time order, to the most recent event.
2. When asked to describe the sequence of events, the witness related each event in the order in which it occurred.
3. When you summarize a work, you give a brief statement of the most important events or ideas.
4. A characteristic is a quality that makes something recognizable.
5. To focus on a scene is to look at it carefully.

Build Language Skills: Grammar, p. 90

A. 1. ? interrogative
2. . declarative
3. ! exclamatory
4. . declarative
5. *or* ! imperative
6. . declarative
7. ? interrogative

B. Students' dialogues should include all four kinds of sentences, with each sentence correctly identified.

Selection Test A, p. 91

Critical Reading

1. ANS: C	DIF: Easy	OBJ: Comprehension
2. ANS: B	DIF: Easy	OBJ: Literary Analysis
3. ANS: A	DIF: Easy	OBJ: Comprehension
4. ANS: B	DIF: Easy	OBJ: Literary Analysis
5. ANS: D	DIF: Easy	OBJ: Interpretation
6. ANS: A	DIF: Easy	OBJ: Reading
7. ANS: C	DIF: Easy	OBJ: Reading
8. ANS: C	DIF: Easy	OBJ: Interpretation
9. ANS: A	DIF: Easy	OBJ: Literary Analysis
10. ANS: B	DIF: Easy	OBJ: Interpretation
11. ANS: A	DIF: Easy	OBJ: Interpretation

Vocabulary and Grammar

12. ANS: C	DIF: Easy	OBJ: Vocabulary
13. ANS: A	DIF: Easy	OBJ: Grammar

Essay

14. Students should recognize that Steve's comment is humorous, at least on the surface, so he is trying to amuse the neighbors, to ease the tension. They may also point out that like his neighbors, Steve is frightened by the inexplicable events and to some extent he may think there is some truth in Tommy's explanation. Therefore, he may also be motivated by a belief in the possibility of a visit by creatures from outer space.

Difficulty: *Easy*
Objective: *Essay*

15. Students should present a well-reasoned explanation of their choice. Those who choose to depict the characters as aliens should allude to the references at the end of the play that suggest that the creatures are indeed aliens. Those who choose to depict them as monsters should refer to the title of the play. Those who choose to depict them as human beings should refer to the message of the play: that we are all capable of being monsters.

Difficulty: *Easy*
Objective: *Essay*

Selection Test B, p. 94

Critical Reading

1. ANS: B	DIF: Challenging	OBJ: Comprehension
2. ANS: C	DIF: Average	OBJ: Literary Analysis
3. ANS: B	DIF: Average	OBJ: Interpretation
4. ANS: C	DIF: Average	OBJ: Reading
5. ANS: B	DIF: Average	OBJ: Literary Analysis
6. ANS: D	DIF: Average	OBJ: Reading
7. ANS: B	DIF: Challenging	OBJ: Interpretation
8. ANS: C	DIF: Challenging	OBJ: Reading
9. ANS: A	DIF: Average	OBJ: Literary Analysis
10. ANS: A	DIF: Challenging	OBJ: Interpretation
11. ANS: A	DIF: Challenging	OBJ: Interpretation

12. ANS: D   DIF: Average   OBJ: Interpretation

13. ANS: B   DIF: Challenging   OBJ: Comprehension

Vocabulary and Grammar

14. ANS: A   DIF: Average   OBJ: Vocabulary

15. ANS: D   DIF: Challenging   OBJ: Vocabulary

16. ANS: C   DIF: Challenging   OBJ: Grammar

Essay

17. Students should recognize that fear has taken over the town and no one is thinking rationally; everyone is reacting emotionally. Charlie accuses Tommy to redirect the crowd's anger, which had been focused on him. The neighbors are ready to believe Charlie because Tommy was the one who had told them about the aliens' methods. Especially perceptive students may recognize that the neighbors willingly believe Charlie because he has not accused any of them.

    Difficulty: *Average*

    Objective: *Essay*

18. Students should coherently describe their initial ideas about the cause of the mysterious events and then describe what they thought when they discovered at the end of the play that aliens seem to have been responsible for the events.

    Difficulty: *Average*

    Objective: *Essay*

from *Our Town* by Thornton Wilder
"My Head Is Full of Starshine" by Peg Kehret

Vocabulary Warm-up Exercises, p. 98

A. 1. practical
   2. expensive
   3. decent
   4. disturb
   5. notices
   6. items
   7. fines
   8. appetite

B. Sample Answers
   1. If I make reservations in advance, it is likely I will not wait for a table because the reservation would be made before I arrive.
   2. If I play according to the rules, my opponent is not likely to get angry because I would be doing what the rules tell me to do.
   3. If someone constantly reminds me of my faults, I am not likely to remain friendly with that person because it is no fun to constantly hear about the things I do wrong.

4. If I am experiencing a strong emotion, it is likely I am feeling too much to be bored.
5. If someone is living in misery, he or she is suffering and is too sad to be enjoying life.
6. If I am abruptly interrupted during an oral report, I would likely be distracted and therefore upset.
7. If an action is critical to my plan, then it is something I must do and not avoid because it is essential.

Reading Warm-up A, p. 99

Sample Answers
1. (Janie); I am practical in the way I save my money.
2. (gold pins); I think gold pins would be costly for a lot of kids.
3. on her "TO DO" list; Two items that might appear on the list are (1) advertise the club in the school newspaper and (2) post notices about the club on the school bulletin board.
4. The Juice Bar on 8th Street; A decent café is clean and serves good food.
5. (the owner); A synonym for *disturb* is *bother.*
6. (talking); Playing a game of soccer gives me an *appetite.*
7. for overdue books; Other kinds of *fines* might be for speeding, late payments, or being overdrawn at the bank.
8. telling people when and where to go for the first meeting; Two notices announcing the meeting might say: (1) Get the buzz. Come to the first meeting of The Buzz Club; or (2) Find out what all the buzzing is about. Come to our first meeting!

Reading Warm-up B, p. 100

Sample Answers
1. Somerset Maugham; *According to* means "as shown or said by someone."
2. a blank page awaiting your thoughts; An antonym for *misery* is *joy.*
3. (any writer), experience; To be a writer you need *potential* or the ability to write, but experience helps develop your writing skills.
4. (strengths); One of my *faults* is putting off the chores I don't like to do.
5. to know in advance what the story is about; *Critical* means "very important."
6. (before); Whenever I want to visit my friends, I always call them *in advance.*
7. (message); The message is never *suddenly* stated; instead, it rises out of the story like an emotion rises out of the body.
8. (out of the body); Stories about abused or abandoned animals always fill me with *emotion.*

Literary Analysis: Comparing Dramatic Speeches, p. 101

Sample Answers

1. The audience learns that George is concerned about Emily's treatment of him; honesty is important to him; he admires Emily for being honest with him; he has been preoccupied with playing baseball; people think he is stuck-up; he likes Emily.

2. The audience learns about George's character from what he and Emily say.

3. The audience learns that Emily does not like the way George has been behaving; she is honest; she is nervous; she cares about how people feel; she is sensitive; she is sorry that she may have hurt George's feelings by speaking honestly; she likes George.

4. The audience learns about Emily's character from what she, George, and the stage manager say.

5. Pam says that the speaker's head is "full of starshine," by which she means that the speaker is dreamy and vague.

6. Pam is practical, orderly, prompt, well organized, focused, and good at science. The descriptions are important because they tell a lot about each girl.

7. The speaker says that she is dreamy; she does not return library books on time; she does not plan what she will wear to a party; she has written a poem as a birthday gift for a friend; she is disturbed when people talk about insects eating other insects; she daydreams to avoid listening to science lessons on that topic; she forgets to bring notices from school to her mother; she makes notes about stories and poems she plans to write; she loves writing assignments.

8. The speaker suggests that she is happy with herself, although she wishes she would remember to return library books on time.

Vocabulary Builder, p. 102

A. Sample Answers

1. Yes; if I accidentally threw away a diamond ring, I would likely be found searching through the trash.

2. No; a realistic person would not ordinarily daydream and procrastinate.

3. No; someone who has little concern for himself or herself and cares about others is not likely to have an excessively high opinion of himself or herself.

4. Yes; someone who shows himself or herself to have the capability of being a great athlete may compete in the Olympics someday.

B. 1. D; 2. B; 3. C; 4. A

Selection Test A, p. 104

Critical Reading

1. ANS: B	DIF: Easy		OBJ: Comprehension
2. ANS: A	DIF: Easy		OBJ: Interpretation

3. ANS: D	DIF: Easy	OBJ: Comprehension
4. ANS: B	DIF: Easy	OBJ: Literary Analysis
5. ANS: C	DIF: Easy	OBJ: Interpretation
6. ANS: A	DIF: Easy	OBJ: Literary Analysis
7. ANS: D	DIF: Easy	OBJ: Interpretation
8. ANS: B	DIF: Easy	OBJ: Comprehension
9. ANS: C	DIF: Easy	OBJ: Comprehension
10. ANS: A	DIF: Easy	OBJ: Comprehension
11. ANS: A	DIF: Easy	OBJ: Literary Analysis
12. ANS: D	DIF: Easy	OBJ: Literary Analysis

Vocabulary

13. ANS: B	DIF: Easy	OBJ: Vocabulary
14. ANS: D	DIF: Easy	OBJ: Vocabulary
15. ANS: B	DIF: Easy	OBJ: Vocabulary

Essay

16. Students should recognize that Emily is giving her speech because George has asked her why she has been treating him differently, and she wants to be honest with him. This speech reveals that Emily cares enough about George to tell him the truth even if it might hurt his feelings. The speaker of "My Head Is Full of Starshine" offers the comparison of Pam and her to point out their differences. The speech reveals that the speaker is forgetful and impractical but creative.

    Difficulty: *Easy*

    Objective: *Essay*

17. Students should explain that *Our Town* is a dialogue because it is a conversation between characters, whereas "My Head Is Full of Starshine" is a monologue because it is a long, uninterrupted speech by a single character. Students should state which work they prefer, and why.

    Difficulty: *Easy*

    Objective: *Essay*

Selection Test B, p. 107

Critical Reading

1. ANS: D	DIF: Average	OBJ: Interpretation
2. ANS: B	DIF: Challenging	OBJ: Interpretation
3. ANS: D	DIF: Challenging	OBJ: Literary Analysis
4. ANS: A	DIF: Average	OBJ: Comprehension
5. ANS: A	DIF: Average	OBJ: Interpretation
6. ANS: B	DIF: Challenging	OBJ: Literary Analysis
7. ANS: D	DIF: Challenging	OBJ: Literary Analysis
8. ANS: D	DIF: Average	OBJ: Interpretation
9. ANS: A	DIF: Average	OBJ: Comprehension
10. ANS: B	DIF: Average	OBJ: Comprehension

11. ANS: D	DIF: Average	OBJ: Interpretation
12. ANS: B	DIF: Average	OBJ: Literary Analysis
13. ANS: C	DIF: Average	OBJ: Literary Analysis
14. ANS: A	DIF: Challenging	OBJ: Literary Analysis

Vocabulary

15. ANS: D	DIF: Challenging	OBJ: Vocabulary
16. ANS: B	DIF: Challenging	OBJ: Vocabulary
17. ANS: D	DIF: Average	OBJ: Vocabulary

Essay

18. Students should define monologues and dialogues according to the definitions in their textbooks and should correctly identify each selection. They might say that the excerpt from *Our Town* is a dialogue because it is a conversation between three characters and because the conversation reveals George's and Emily's traits. They might say that "My Head Is Full of Starshine" is a monologue because it is a long, uninterrupted speech by one character, and it reveals her private thoughts and feelings.

Difficulty: *Average*

Objective: *Essay*

19. Students should recognize that the conflict between George and Emily has to do with George's changed behavior and Emily's response to it. The conflict is resolved when George asks Emily why she has treated him differently lately and she tells him. Students should recognize that the conflict between the speaker in "My Head Is Full of Sunshine" and Pam has to do with the characters' differences. At the start of the monologue, it is clear that Pam has accepted their differences, but the conflict is resolved for the speaker only at the end, when she announces that she is largely happy with herself as she is. Students should state which friendship they prefer and offer a well-reasoned explanation of their choice.

Difficulty: *Challenging*

Objective: *Literary Analysis*

Writing Workshop—Unit 5, Part 2

Cause-and-Effect Essay: Integrating Grammar Skills, p. 111

A. 1. combine; 2. sell; 3. like; 4. produces; 5. is

B. 1. Milk and cheese often come from Wisconsin and Vermont.

2. Neither Wisconsin nor Vermont produces as much beef as Texas.

3. Either Brazil or Argentina is known for beef.

4. Neither Australia nor the British Isles have as many cows as Canada.

Spelling Workshop—Unit 5

Vowel Sounds in Unstressed Syllables, p. 112

A. 1. vitamin; 2. quotient; 3. attorney; 4. sensitive; 5. vertical; 6. bulletin; 7. sponsor; 8. amusing; 9. captain; 10. disease

B. Answers will vary.

Unit 5, Part 2 Answers

Benchmark Test 10, p. 115

MULTIPLE CHOICE

1. ANS: B
2. ANS: C
3. ANS: D
4. ANS: B
5. ANS: C
6. ANS: C
7. ANS: A
8. ANS: D
9. ANS: D
10. ANS: B
11. ANS: B
12. ANS: D
13. ANS: C
14. ANS: B
15. ANS: A
16. ANS: D
17. ANS: C
18. ANS: A
19. ANS: C
20. ANS: B
21. ANS: B
22. ANS: B
23. ANS: D
24. ANS: C
25. ANS: B
26. ANS: B
27. ANS: C
28. ANS: A
29. ANS: B

ESSAY

30. Students' paragraphs should describe a plan for writing a report. The paragraphs should include a plan for gathering information, an organizational plan, and at least two recommended changes for improving their neighborhood.

31. Students should choose one among several possible topics for a cause-and-effect essay. They should then write a sentence in which they tell why the topic interests them. Finally, they should list at least three questions related to the topic and to the type of essay.

32. Students' topic webs should show one main topic in a center circle, with at least four ideas or questions radiating from the main topic in additional circles that are connected to the main circle by lines. All of the ideas or questions should be related to the main topic.

CURRICULUM